Revision Questions for Higher Chemistry

D A Buchanan
(Moray House School of Education,
University of Edinburgh)

J R Melrose
(formerly Lenzie Academy)

Published by
Chemcord
Inch Keith
East Kilbride
Glasgow

ISBN 9781870570961

Printed by Bell and Bain Ltd, Glasgow

Note to teachers / students

* The questions are specifically written to test students' understanding of the key ideas in the Higher Chemistry course,

* The aim is to give students practice in the kinds of question used in the Higher examination and other course assessments.

* The questions have also been found to be an invaluable revision aid.

* The questions cover both Knowledge and understanding and Problem solving.

* The exercises are, by and large, independent of each other and consequently they can be used to fit almost any teaching order. Hey can be used in a variety of situations, e.g. for examination revision, self-study time in school, homework, etc.

* Some questions refer to the Data Booklet. This can be downloaded from the SQA website.

  (http://www.sqa.org.uk/files_ccc/ChemistryDataBookletSQPH.pdf)

* Questions in "The Avogadro constant (ii)" on page 75 are not part of the mandatory content of the course. However, given the Avogadro constant, students could perhaps meet calculations of this kind in a problem-solving context.

* A complete set of answers is available in the publication *"Answers to Revision Questions for Higher Chemistry"*. Answers are structured with sufficient detail to assist the student in their understanding of the related content.

Acknowledgement

A number of questions in the exercises come from or have evolved from questions used in Scottish Qualifications Authority (SQA) examinations. The publisher wishes to thank the SQA for permission to use the examination questions in this way.

Index

Chemical Changes and Structure

Nature's Chemistry

Chemistry in Society

Successful collisions

1. (a) Describe a laboratory reaction that can be used to investigate the effect of decreasing the particle size of a reactant on the rate of reaction.
    (b) What is the conclusion?
    (c) Use collision theory to explain the effect.

2. (a) Describe a laboratory reaction that can be used to investigate the effect of decreasing the concentration of a reactant on the rate of reaction.
    (b) What is the conclusion?
    (c) Use collision theory to explain the effect.

3. (a) Describe a laboratory reaction that can be used to investigate the effect of increasing the temperature of a reactant on the rate of reaction.
    (b) What is the conclusion?

4. (a) i)   What term is given to the minimum kinetic energy required for a successful collision to occur between particles?
        ii) What is this energy required to do?
    (b) In addition to reactant molecules having the necessary minimum kinetic energy, what other condition may be necessary for a successful collision to occur?

5. A collision is a **necessary** but not **sufficient** condition for two different molecules to react to form a product.
    Explain this statement.

6. A student wrote the following statement in answer to a question.

    The increase in reaction rate with increasing temperature is due to an increase in the rate of collisions.

    (a) Do you agree with this statement?
    (b) Explain your answer.

7. The rates of many reactions are roughly doubled for a 10 $^{\circ}$C rise in temperature.
    With the help of an energy distribution diagram, explain why a small temperature rise can have such a great effect on reaction rate.

Reaction profiles

1. State what is meant by
   (a) an exothermic reaction,
   (b) an endothermic reaction.

2. In terms of bond breaking and bond making, explain why a reaction is
   (a) exothermic,
   (b) endothermic.

3. State what is meant by
   (a) the enthalpy of a substance,
   (b) the enthalpy change of a reaction.

4. Give the sign for the enthalpy change of
   (a) an exothermic reaction,
   (b) an endothermic reaction.

5. The activation energy for a forward reaction is +236 kJ mol^{-1} and the activation energy for the reverse reaction is +92 kJ mol^{-1}.
   (a) What is the enthalpy change for the forward reaction?
   (b) Is the forward reaction endothermic or exothermic?

6. The activation energy and the enthalpy change for a forward reaction are +80 kJ mol^{-1} and -20 kJ mol^{-1} respectively.
   (a) Present this information on graph paper to show the potential energy diagram for the reaction.
   (b) What is the activation energy for the reverse reaction?

7. The potential energy diagram refers to an industrial reaction.

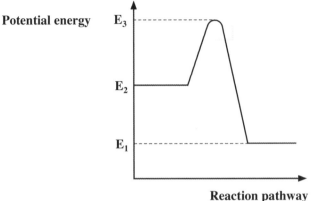

In terms of E_1, E_2 and E_3, state
(a) the activation energy for the forward reaction,
(b) the enthalpy change for the reverse reaction.

8. The following potential energy diagram refers to the uncatalysed decomposition of hydrogen peroxide.

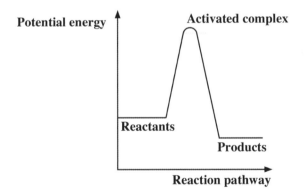

(a) Copy the potential energy diagram and add a curve to represent the decomposition when a catalyst is added to the hydrogen peroxide solution.
(b) What is meant by the activated complex?

9. State the effect of a catalyst on
    (a) the activation energy of a reaction,
    (b) the enthalpy change of a reaction.

10. Consider the following potential energy diagram.

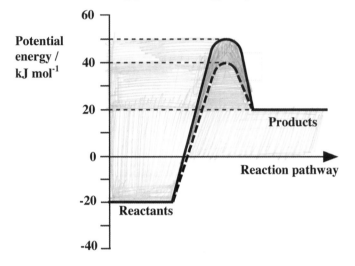

    (a) State the value of the activation energy for
        i)   the uncatalysed forward reaction,
        ii) the uncatalysed reverse reaction,
        iii) the catalysed forward reaction,
        iv) the catalysed reverse reaction.
    (b) State the value for the enthalpy change of
        i)   the forward reaction,
        ii) the reverse reaction.

11. Inhibitors can be thought of as negative catalysts. They are commonly
    added to plastics to slow down thermal degradation.
    For the degradation reaction, state the effect of such inhibitors on
    (a) the enthalpy change,
    (b) the activation energy.

12. The diagram shows the energy changes involved in an uncatalysed reaction and also in the catalysed reaction.

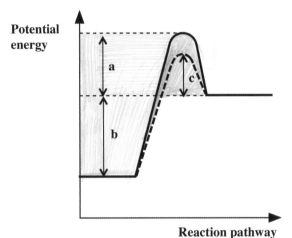

Reaction pathway

(a) State the value (in terms of **a**, **b**, and **c**) of
   i)   the activation energy of the uncatalysed forward reaction,
   ii) the activation energy of the catalysed reverse reaction,
   iii) the enthalpy change for the forward reaction.
(b) Is the forward reaction exothermic or endothermic?

The arrangement of elements in the Periodic Table (revision)

1. (a) What **TWO** 'features' of elements did Mendeleev use in drawing up the early Periodic Table?
   (b) What is the present-day basis for the arrangement of elements?

2. Why do elements in the same group have similar chemical properties?

3. State the name given to the elements
   (a) in Group 1 of the Periodic Table,
   (b) in Group 7 of the Periodic Table,
   (c) in Group 0 of the Periodic Table.

4. (a) In what way does the density of elements change going across Periods 2 and 3 of the Periodic Table?
   (b) In what way does the melting point of elements change going down Group 1 of the Periodic Table?
   (c) In what way does the boiling point of elements change going down Group 7 of the Periodic Table?

(You may wish to refer to the Data Booklet.)

Bonding and structure in the first twenty elements

1. (a) From the first twenty elements, name an element with
      i) a single covalent bond between the atoms,
      ii) a double covalent bond between the atoms,
      iii) a triple covalent bond between the atoms.
   (b) From the first twenty elements, name the element made up of
      i) four atom molecules,
      ii) eight atom molecules.

2. (a) Describe the bonding and structure in a metal element.
   (b) Why do metals conduct electricity both as solids and liquids?

3. Use the Data Booklet to find the melting point of lithium, sodium and potassium.
   (a) Going down the group from lithium to sodium state what must happen to the strength of the metallic bonds.
   (b) Explain why this happens.

4. (a) What is meant by a covalent network structure?
   (b) From the first twenty elements, name **TWO** elements with a covalent network structure.
   (c) Why do elements with a covalent network structure have very high melting points?

5. (a) i) Describe the structure of diamond.
      ii) Draw a diagram to show the structure.
   (b) Give a property of diamond and a use related to this property.

6. (a) Draw a diagram to show the structure of graphite.
   (b) Explain why graphite
      i) conducts electricity but diamond does not,
      ii) can be used as a lubricant and as 'lead' in pencils.

7. New forms of carbon have recently been made. They exist as individual molecules of different sizes and are called fullerenes. The main fullerene has the formula C_{60}.
    In what way does the structure of a fullerene differ from that of diamond?

8.

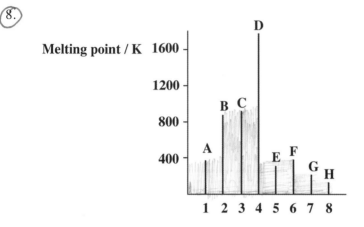

    The graph shows the melting points for the elements across a period in the Periodic Table.

    a) Identify the period represented by the graph.
    b) The bonding in both elements **A** and **B** is metallic.
        Explain why the melting point of element **B** is higher than that of element **A**.
    c) Elements **D** and **E** are both covalently bonded.
        In terms of structure, account for the large difference in their melting points.

9. Use a data booklet to find the melting points of chlorine, phosphorus, magnesium and silicon.
    (a) Explain why the melting points of chlorine and phosphorus are relatively low.
    (b) Explain why the melting points of each of magnesium and silicon are relatively high.

10. In the second period, the melting points of boron and carbon are much higher than the melting points of nitrogen, oxygen and fluorine.
    Explain why this is so.

11. Copy and complete each line in the table with **TWO** elements from the first 20 in the Periodic Table.

Type of bonding and structure	Elements
Metals	
Covalent network solids	
Covalent molecular solids	
Diatomic gases	
Monatomic gases	

Covalent and ionic radius

1. (a) What is meant by the covalent radius of an atom?
    (b) Draw a graph of covalent radius (y-axis) against atomic number for the elements 3 to 20, using information from the Data Booklet. (Use a dotted line between atomic numbers 9 and 11, and 17 and 19.)
    (c) Why is the covalent radius of an atom an example of a periodic property?

2. Describe the trend in covalent radius of atoms of the elements
    (a) on crossing a period in the Periodic Table from left to right,
    (b) on descending a group in the Periodic Table.

3. In which part of the Periodic Table is each of the following to be found?
    (a) the element made up of atoms with the smallest covalent radius
    (b) the element made up of atoms with the largest covalent radius

4. Explain why
    (a) a lithium atom is larger than a fluorine atom,
    (b) a fluorine atom is smaller than an iodine atom.

5. Explain why
    (a) a fluoride ion is smaller than a chloride ion,
    (b) a lithium ion is smaller than a fluoride ion,
    (c) a potassium ion is larger than a calcium ion,
    (d) a chloride ion is larger than a potassium ion.

6. The graph below relates the ionic radius of some elements to their atomic numbers.

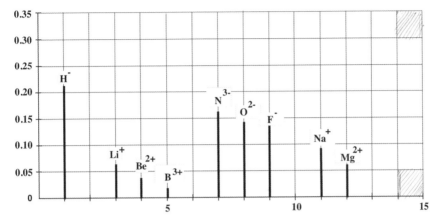

(a) State the ionic radius you would predict for each of the ions of the elements with atomic numbers 13 and 15.
(b) The value quoted above for hydrogen is for the hydride ion (H^-).
    i) Why is no value given for the H^+ ion?
    ii) Why is the H^- ion larger than the Li^+ ion?
(c) Why is there a large increase in ionic radius from boron to nitrogen?

7. On crossing the Periodic Table there are trends in ionic radii.
(a) Explain why the ions of sodium, magnesium and aluminium are much smaller than their corresponding atoms.
(b) Explain why there is a large increase in ionic radius from aluminium, Al^{3+}, to phosphorus, P^{3-}.
(c) i) What do all the ions from nitrogen, N^{3-}, to aluminium, Al^{3+}, have in common?
    ii) Explain why the ionic radii tend to decrease along this sequence.

Ionisation energy and electronegativity

1. (a) What is meant by the first ionisation energy of an element?
    (b) i) Is the process involved exothermic or endothermic?
        ii) Explain your answer.

2. (a) Using the information in the Data Booklet, draw a graph of
        the first ionisation energy (y-axis) against atomic number for
        the first twenty elements.
        (Use a dotted line between the noble gases and the elements
        in Group 1.)
    (b) Why is the first ionisation energy of an element an example of a
        periodic property?

3. Describe the trend in first ionisation energy of atoms of the elements
    (a) on crossing a period in the Periodic Table from left to right,
    (b) on descending a group in the Periodic Table.

4. Explain why
    (a) a lithium atom has a larger first ionisation energy than a potassium
        atom,
    (b) an aluminium atom has a larger first ionisation energy than a sodium
        atom.

5. Explain the large difference between
    (a) i)   the first and second ionisation energies of lithium,
        ii) the second and third ionisation energies of calcium,
        iii) the third and fourth ionisation energies of aluminium.
    (b) Why is there no value given in the Data Booklet for the fourth
        ionisation energy of lithium?

6. (a) Write an equation corresponding to
        i)   the first ionisation energy of sodium,
        ii) the second ionisation energy of magnesium,
        iii) the third ionisation energy of aluminium.
    (b) Refer to the Data Booklet and alongside each of the above equations
        write in the ΔH value with its appropriate sign.

7. Calculate the energy required to bring about the following changes.
   (a) $Al(g) \rightarrow Al^{3+}(g) + 3e^-$
   (b) $K^+(g) \rightarrow K^{3+}(g) + 2e^-$

8. (a) What is meant by the electronegativity of an atom?
   (b) Using the information in the Data Booklet, draw a graph of electronegativity (y-axis) against atomic number for the first twenty elements.
   (Use a dotted line between the noble gases and the elements in Group 1.)
   (c) Why is the electronegativity of an atom an example of a periodic property?
   (d) Which group in the Periodic Table has elements with no quoted values for electronegativity?

9. Describe the trend in electronegativity values of atoms of the elements
   (a) on crossing a period in the Periodic Table from left to right,
   (b) on descending a group in the Periodic Table.

10. Explain why a fluorine atom has a larger electronegativity value than
    (a) a chlorine atom,
    (b) an oxygen atom.

11. The enthalpy of electron gain is the energy released when each atom in one mole of gaseous atoms of the element gains one electron.
    Write an equation corresponding to the enthalpy of electron gain for chlorine.

Covalent and ionic bonding (revision)

1. (a) Taking hydrogen sulphide as an example, describe what happens in the formation of a covalent bond.
    (b) Describe the forces of attraction in a covalent bond.

2. (a) Taking sodium chloride as an example, describe what happens in the formation of an ionic bond.
    (b) Why are ionic bonds strong?
    (c) Why has the word 'molecule' no meaning when applied to sodium chloride?

3. Consider the following list of substances.

    hydrogen oxide, chlorine, sodium fluoride, fluorine, potassium chloride, nitrogen chloride, oxygen, lithium oxide, hydrogen sulphide

    Identify the substances that have bonding and structure that can be described as
    (a) covalent molecular,
    (b) ionic lattice.

4. (a) What is the difference between a covalent molecular compound and a covalent network compound?
    (b) Name **TWO** covalent network compounds.

5. Copy and complete the table to show the bonding and structure of the three oxides at room temperature.

Oxide	Bonding and structure
Na_2O	*ionic lattice*
CO_2	*covalent molecule*
SiO_2	*covalent / structure*

Polar covalent bonds and the bonding continuum

1. (a) What is meant by a polar covalent bond?
    (b) i)   Using hydrogen fluoride as an example, explain why there is a polar covalent bond in the molecule.
         ii) Draw a diagram to show how the polarity of the bond can be represented in the molecule.
    (c) i)   Which is the more polar bond, H-F or H-Cl?
         ii) Explain your answer.

2. (a) What is meant by a permanent dipole?
    (b) Explain why the water molecule has a permanent dipole.

3. Explain why NH_3 has polar covalent bonds and yet both nitrogen and hydrogen do not.

4. (a) Explain why phosphorus hydride does **not** contain polar covalent bonds.
    (b) i)   Name a compound of carbon that does **not** contain polar covalent bonds.
         ii) Name a compound of nitrogen that does **not** contain polar covalent bonds.

         (You may wish to refer to page 11 of the Data Booklet.)

5. Explain why potassium fluoride is more ionic in character than lithium bromide.

6. (a) Which two elements in the second period will form the compound with most ionic character.
    (b) Give a reason for your choice.

7. Explain why you would expect rubidium fluoride to be the most ionic of the halides of rubidium.

Polar molecules

1. Explain why a molecule with polar bonds can be overall non-polar .

2. By drawing the shape and considering the symmetry, decide whether each of the following molecules is polar.
   (a) ammonia (NH_3)
   (b) silicon tetrachloride ($SiCl_4$)

3. The bonds in both water and carbon dioxide are polar.
   With the help of diagrams, explain why water molecules are polar but carbon dioxide molecules are non-polar.

4. Explain why carbon tetrachloride molecules (CCl_4) are non-polar but chloroform molecules ($CHCl_3$) are polar.

5. Explain why hexane molecules can be considered to be non-polar but hexanol molecules are polar.

6. A jet of water from a burette is deflected when a charged rod is held close to it. Other liquids treated a similar way gave the following results.

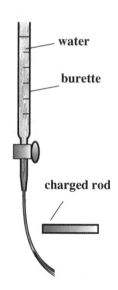

water

burette

Group A	Group B
water	cyclohexane
propanone	hexene
ethanol	pentane
trichloromethane	

charged rod

   (a) Why are the liquids in Group **A** deflected but those in Group **B** are not?
   (b) Explain what would happen with a jet of tetrachloromethane.

7. The cyclohexane ring is a symmetrical arrangement of carbon and hydrogen atoms. The hydrogen atoms can be replaced by one or more chlorine atoms.
Two dichlorocyclohexane isomers are shown.

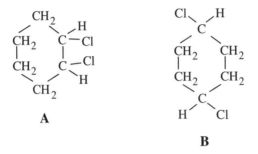

A

B

Explain why molecule **A** is polar while molecule **B** is non-polar.

Intermolecular forces of attraction

1. (a) What name is given to all types of intermolecular forces?
   (b) How do the strengths of intermolecular forces compare with the strengths of covalent bonds?

2. (a) What is meant by London dispersion forces?
   (b) What causes these forces?

3. Describe the trend in the strengths of the London dispersion forces
   (a) i) as the number of carbon atoms in an alkane increases,
       ii) going down the halogen group in the Periodic Table,
   (b) Explain your answers.

4. (a) What is meant by permanent dipole-permanent dipole interactions?
   (b) How do the strengths of permanent dipole-permanent dipole interactions compare with the strengths of London dispersion forces?

5. (a) What name is given to the strongest form of permanent dipole-permanent dipole interactions?
   (b) Explain why these permanent dipole-permanent dipole interactions are particularly strong.

6. Explain why ammonia (NH_3) has hydrogen bonding between the molecules and yet there is no such bonding in hydrogen bromide (HBr).

7. (a) Why does hydrogen **not** have hydrogen bonding between the molecules?
   (b) What name is given to the intermolecular forces in hydrogen?

8. H_2, HF, NCl_3, Cl_2, H_2O, PF_3, N_2, HBr, NH_3

Copy the table and place each of the above formulae in the correct column.

London dispersion forces occur	Permanent dipole - permanent dipole interactions occur; no hydrogen bonding	Hydrogen bonding occurs
H_2, Cl_2 N_2, NCl_3	HF PF_3 NCl_3 HBr	H_2O HF NH_3

9. Analysis of hydrogen fluoride, HF, shows the existence of molecules with relative molecular masses of 20, 40 and 60.
Explain the origin of these molecules.

Properties of compounds

1. (a) Explain why ionic compounds have high melting and boiling points.
    (b) Explain why ionic compounds can conduct electricity when molten but **not** in the solid form.

2. (a) Explain why covalent molecular compounds have relatively low melting and boiling points.
    (b) Explain why covalent molecular compounds **cannot** conduct electricity in any form.

3. Explain why covalent network compounds have very high melting points compared with covalent molecular compounds.

4. Compound **X** has a melting point of 1700 °C and does **not** conduct electricity when molten.
    (a) State the type of bonding and structure that exist in compound **X**.
    (b) Explain your answer.

5.

	Melting point / °C	Boiling point / °C
Sodium chloride	801	1417
Carbon tetrachloride	-23	77

From the above information, a student deduced that ionic bonding must be stronger than covalent bonding.
Explain whether or not you agree with this conclusion.

6. Titanium chloride, $TiCl_4$, is a colourless liquid which boils at 132 °C. Explain whether the bonding in titanium chloride is likely to be ionic or covalent.

7. The table shows the melting points of lithium halides.

Halide	Melting point / $^{\circ}$C
LiF	842
LiCl	614
LiBr	547
LiI	450

Explain the trend in the melting points.

8. Explain why phosphorus trichloride has a melting point of -91 $^{\circ}$C but sodium chloride has a melting point of 801 $^{\circ}$C.

9. (a) Explain the trend in the boiling points of hydrogen halides going down the group from hydrogen chloride to hydrogen iodide.
    (b) Explain the unexpectedly high boiling point of hydrogen fluoride.

10.

Compound	Formula	Molecular mass	Boiling point / $^{\circ}$C
ethane	CH_3CH_3	30	-89
methanol	CH_3OH	32	64
hydrazine	NH_2NH_2	32	113
silane	SiH_4	32	-112

(a) From the information given, which of the compounds in the table contain hydrogen bonding in the liquid state?
(b) Why does hydrogen bonding affect the boiling point of a substance?
(c) The table compares substances of similar molecular mass.
     Why is it important, in this case, to compare compounds of similar molecular mass?

11. Liquid ammonia boils at -33 $^{\circ}$C but liquid phosphine, PH_3, boils at -87.5 $^{\circ}$C.
    Explain this difference in terms of bonding.

12. Explain why the boiling point of hydrogen peroxide, H_2O_2 (150 °C), is much higher than that of hydrogen sulphide, H_2S (- 61 °C), which has the same molecular mass.

13.

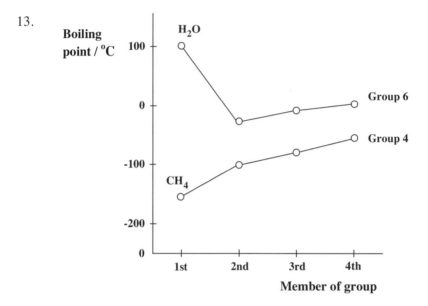

The graph shows the boiling points of the hydrides of elements in Groups 4 and 6 of the Periodic Table.

(a) Why is there a fairly steady increase in the boiling points of the Group 4 hydrides on going down the group?

(b) What causes water to have a boiling point considerably higher than expected?

14.

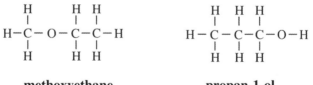

methoxyethane   **propan-1-ol**

Predict which of the above isomers will have the higher boiling point and explain your choice.

15. A student is comparing the boiling points of alkanes and alcohols to examine the influence of hydrogen bonding.
    (a) Why do the boiling points of the alkanes increase with increasing molecular mass?
    (b) Which of the two families has hydrogen bonding between the molecules?
    (c) i) To examine the influence of hydrogen bonding, the boiling point of which alcohol should be compared with that of butane?
        ii) Explain your answer.

16. Maleic acid and fumaric acid have the same molecular formula. Their structures are different because rotation is **not** possible about the carbon-carbon double bond.

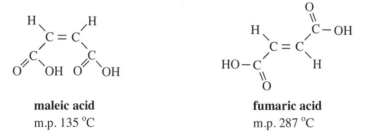

    maleic acid   **fumaric acid**
    m.p. 135 °C   m.p. 287 °C

    (a) The molecular mass of octane (melting point -57 °C) is the nearly the same as that of the two acids.
        Why is the melting point of octane significantly lower than the melting point of the acids?
    (b) Why is the melting point of fumaric acid higher than that of maleic acid?

17. Paraffin wax and petrol are both made up of hydrocarbon molecules. Explain why paraffin wax is a solid and yet petrol is a liquid at room temperature.

18. Explain why ice floats on water.

19. Methanol, CH_3OH, can be used as an alternative fuel in car engines. It is less volatile than petrol and less likely to explode in a car accident. Explain why methanol is less volatile than petrol.

20.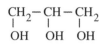

       ethanol   **propane-1,2,3-triol**   **ethane-1,2-diol**

    (a) Describe an experiment that could be carried out to compare the viscosities of the three alcohols.

    (b) Arrange the alcohols in order of increasing viscosity.

21. Taking sodium chloride as an example, explain what happens when an ionic solid dissolves in water.

22. Explain each of the following.

    (a) Potassium fluoride is soluble in water but **not** in hexane.

    (b) Tetrachloromethane is soluble in hexane but **not** in water.

23. Lithium iodide is moderately soluble in non-polar solvents. What does this suggest about the bonding in the compound?

24. Poly(ethenol) has the following structure.

$$\begin{array}{cccccc} H & OH & H & OH & H & OH \\ | & | & | & | & | & | \\ -C- & C- & C- & C- & C- & C- \\ | & | & | & | & | & | \\ H & H & H & H & H & H \end{array}$$

Explain why poly(ethenol) dissolves in water but poly(ethene) is insoluble.

25. Explain why silicon dioxide is used as an abrasive.

26. Taking hydrogen chloride as an example, explain why compounds with highly polar covalent bonds dissolve in water to form acid solutions.

Problem solving : factors affecting rate

1. The following graph shows how the volume of the hydrogen produced in the reaction of excess magnesium with dilute acid varies with time.

    Volume of hydrogen produced / cm³

    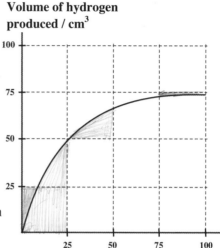

    Time / s

    (a) What is the total volume of hydrogen produced in the reaction?

    (b) i)   How long does it take for the reaction to go to completion?

         ii) How long does it take for half of the hydrogen ions in the acid to be reduced to hydrogen?

    (c) Explain why your answer to part ii) is not half your answer to part i).

2. The overall rate of a reaction is often taken as the reciprocal of time (1/time).
    A graph of rate of reaction against temperature is shown opposite.

    Rate / s⁻¹

    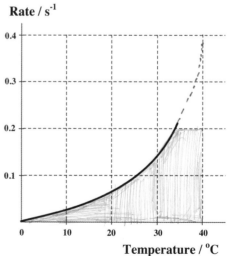

    Temperature / °C

    (a) Calculate the time for the reaction when the temperature is 20 °C.

    (b) Estimate the temperature rise required to double the rate of the reaction.

    (c) Predict the rate of the reaction at 40 °C.

3. The rate of reaction between calcium carbonate and excess dilute hydrochloric acid was followed by recording the mass of the container and the reaction mixture over a period of time. The results of an experiment are shown in the graph.

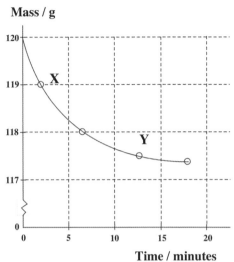

Mass / g

(a) How does the rate of reaction at **X** compare with that at **Y**?

(b) The half-life of the reaction is the time taken for half of the calcium carbonate to be used up.
Calculate the half-life for this reaction.

4. A student carried out a series of experiments to study the effect of changing the concentration of a reactant on the rate of the reaction. A plot of rate against relative concentration of the reactant produced the graph shown.

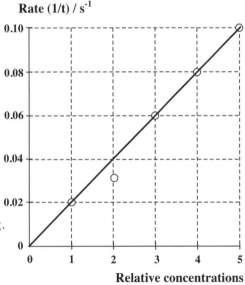

Rate (1/t) / s^{-1}

(a) Predict the rate if the relative concentration had been increased to 8.

(b) The graph suggests that the time recorded for one of the experiments is wrong. Assuming the other points to be correct, what time should have been recorded for this experiment?

5. Excess zinc powder was added to 100 cm^3 of sulphuric acid, concentration 2 mol l^{-1}, at room temperature. The volume of hydrogen produced was plotted against time.

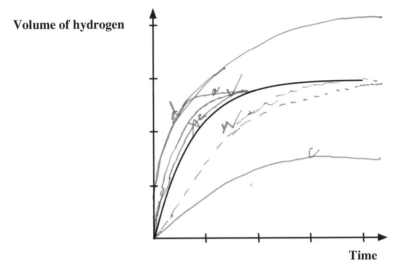

Copy the graph and add the corresponding curves that would be obtained if the reaction was repeated

(a) at a higher temperature,

(b) using zinc granules,

(c) using 100 cm^3 of hydrochloric acid, concentration 2 mol l^{-1},

(d) using 200 cm^3 of sulphuric acid, concentration 2 mol l^{-1}.

6. Four experiments were carried out at room temperature with magnesium carbonate and acids. In each case 10 g (excess) of the carbonate was present at the start. The rate of mass loss was studied for various conditions.

Experiment	Acid	MgCO$_3$
A	20 cm^3 HCl (aq), concentration 1 mol l^{-1}	Powdered
B	20 cm^3 HCl (aq), concentration 1 mol l^{-1}	Lump
C	20 cm^3 H$_2$SO$_4$ (aq), concentration 1 mol l^{-1}	Powdered
D	10 cm^3 HCl (aq), concentration 1 mol l^{-1}	Powdered

The results of Experiment A were plotted on a graph.

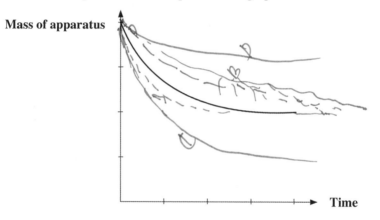

Copy the graph showing reaction A and add the corresponding curves that could have been obtained for each of Experiments B, C and D.

(7) (a) Write balanced equations for the reaction of 1 mol of each of the following metals with an excess of dilute hydrochloric acid.
   i)   magnesium
   ii) zinc
   iii) sodium

(b) The graph below shows how the volume of hydrogen produced as 0.1 mol of magnesium reacts with excess dilute hydrochloric acid varies with time.

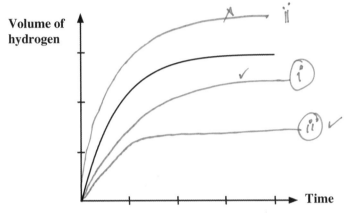

Copy this graph and add corresponding curves for the reactions of
   i)   0.1 mol of zinc, → less reactive
   ii) 0.1 mol of sodium. Double amount of reactants would be needed to form some volume of gas.
        (Assume that the three metals have similar surface areas.)

8. Hydrogen peroxide solution decomposes to produce oxygen gas.

$$2H_2O_2\,(aq) \quad \rightarrow \quad 2H_2O\,(l) \quad + \quad O_2\,(g)$$

The rate of oxygen production was measured in three laboratory experiments using the same volume of hydrogen peroxide solution at the same temperature.

Experiment	Concentration of H_2O_2 / mol 1^{-1}
A	0.2
B	0.4
C	0.6

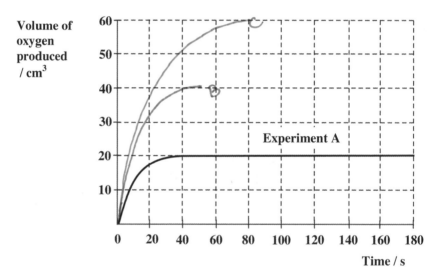

(a) Copy the graph shown for Experiment **A** and add curves to show the results for each of the Experiments **B** and **C**.

(b) In a fourth experiment, **A** was repeated with the temperature increased by 20 °C.
State how this would affect
   i)   the volume of oxygen produced in the first 20 s of the reaction,
   ii) the total volume of oxygen produced.

9. The following graph shows the production of gas, with time, when two 0.5 g samples of calcium carbonate, each containing insoluble impurities, react with excess dilute hydrochloric acid.

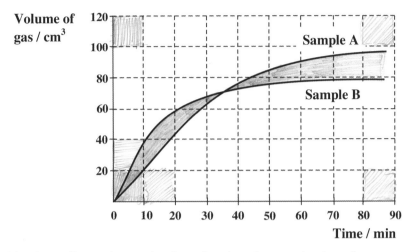

(a) According to the graph, after what time does production of gas cease with sample **B**?

(b) State which of the two samples has
   i) the higher purity,
   ii) the smaller particle size.

(c) Explain your answers to part b).

10. Sodium thiosulphate solution, $Na_2S_2O_3$ (aq), reacts with hydrochloric acid to produce a suspension of sulphur.

$$S_2O_3{}^{2-} (aq) + 2H^+ (aq) \quad \rightarrow \quad S (s) + SO_2 (g) + H_2O (1)$$

The rate of this reaction can be determined from the time it takes the sulphur formed to obscure a cross marked on a sheet of paper underneath the reaction vessel.

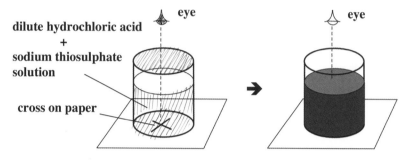

A student carried out a series of experiments and obtained the following results.

	Volume of $Na_2S_2O_3$ used / cm^3	Volume of water added / cm^3	Volume of HCl (aq) added	Time (t) for X to be obscured / s
A	50	0	10	10.0
B	40	10	10	12.5
C	30	20	10	16.7
D	20	30	10	33.3
E	10	40	10	50.0

(a) From the information in the results table, which **TWO** factors were being kept constant throughout the series of experiments?
(b) i) What was the purpose of the investigation?
    ii) What would be the conclusion?

Hydrocarbons (revision)

1. Give the systematic name for each of the following hydrocarbons.

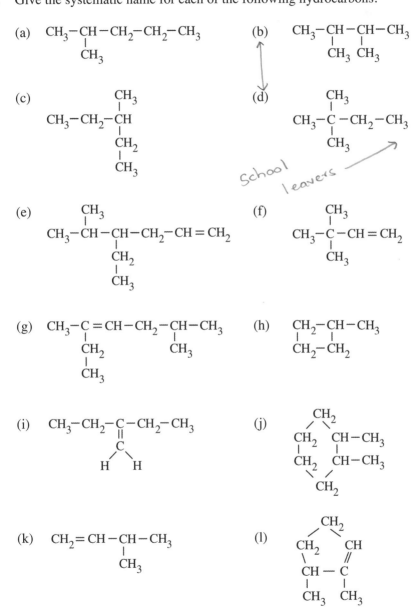

(a) $CH_3-CH-CH_2-CH_2-CH_3$
         |
         CH_3

(b) $CH_3-CH-CH-CH_3$
         | |
         CH_3 CH_3

(c) CH_3
         |
    CH_3-CH_2-CH
              |
              CH_2
              |
              CH_3

(d) CH_3
         |
    $CH_3-C-CH_2-CH_3$
         |
         CH_3

School leavers

(e) CH_3
         |
    $CH_3-CH-CH-CH_2-CH=CH_2$
              |
              CH_2
              |
              CH_3

(f) CH_3
         |
    $CH_3-C-CH=CH_2$
         |
         CH_3

(g) $CH_3-C=CH-CH_2-CH-CH_3$
              | |
              CH_2 CH_3
              |
              CH_3

(h) $CH_2-CH-CH_3$
         | |
         CH_2-CH_2

(i) $CH_3-CH_2-C-CH_2-CH_3$
                   ||
                   C
                  / \
                 H H

(j) CH_2
       /   \
   CH_2 $CH-CH_3$
     | |
   CH_2 $CH-CH_3$
       \   /
        CH_2

(k) $CH_2=CH-CH-CH_3$
                 |
                 CH_3

(l) CH_2
       /   \
   CH_2 CH
     \   //
     CH — C
      | |
     CH_3 CH_3

2. Draw a structural formula for each of the following hydrocarbons.

   (a) methylpropane

   (b) ethylhexane

   (c) 2,2,4-trimethylpentane

   (d) 2-methyl-3-ethylheptane

   (e) pent-l-ene

   (f) 4,4-dimethyloct-1-ene

   (g) 2,3-dimethylbut-2-ene

   (h) 4-methylhex-2-ene

   (i) penta-1,3-diene

   (j) ethylcyclohexane

   (k) cyclopentene

   (l) 1,3-dimethylcyclopentane

3. A ratio line can be used to illustrate the carbon to hydrogen ratio in different hydrocarbons.

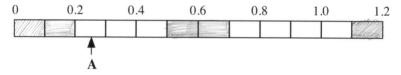

   Methane would appear at point **A**.

   At what value would each of the following hydrocarbons appear?

   (a) ethane

   (b) methylpropane

   (c) 3,3-dimethylhex-1-ene

   (d) methylcyclohexane

   (e) cyclopentene

   (f) buta-1,3-diene

4. A structural formula for 2-methylbutane is:

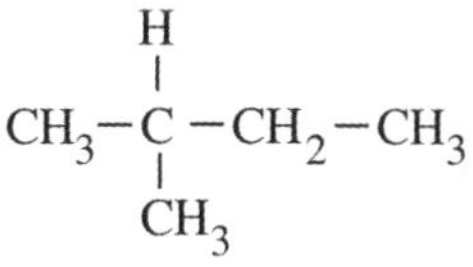

$$\begin{array}{c} \text{H} \\ | \\ CH_3-C-CH_2-CH_3 \\ | \\ CH_3 \end{array}$$

The structural formula can be written without bonds and using brackets to show the position of a branch.

$CH_3CH(CH_3)CH_2CH_3$

Give the systematic name for each of the following hydrocarbons.

(a) $CH_3CH_2C(CH_3)_2CH_2CH_3$

(b) $CH_3CH(CH_3)CH(CH_3)CH(CH_3)_2$

(c) $(CH_3)_2CHCH(CH_3)CH_2CH_3$

(d) $C(CH_3)_4$

(e) $CH_2CHCH_2CH_3$

(f) $(CH_3)_3CCHCHCH_3$

(g) $(CH_3)_2CCH_2$

(h) $(CH_3)_3CCHCH_2$

5. Draw a structural formula for each of the following hydrocarbons and give the systematic name.

(a) the **three** straight-chain isomers of 1,2-dimethylcyclobutane

(b) the **two** straight-chain isomers of cyclopentene

(c) the **three** isomers of C_5H_{12}

(d) the **five** isomers of C_4H_8

Reactions of alkenes (revision)

1. (a) One mole of a straight-chain hydrocarbon **Y** with four carbon atoms
        per molecule reacts with one mole of bromine.
        What can be concluded from this reaction?
    (b) An unbranched hydrocarbon **Z** with six carbon atoms per molecule
        has a general formula C_xH_y. **Z** does **not** immediately decolourise
        bromine solution.
        Give a name for **Z** .

2. The following table gives information about the addition of bromine to
    four different hydrocarbons.

	Molecular formula of hydrocarbon	Compound formed on reaction with bromine
A	C_6H_{12}	$C_6H_{12}Br_2$
B	C_6H_{12}	No product formed
C	C_6H_{10}	$C_6H_{10}Br_4$
D	C_6H_{10}	$C_6H_{10}Br_2$

    Draw a possible structural formula for each of the hydrocarbons **A**, **B**, **C**
    and **D**.

3. (a) Draw the full structural formula for the product when each of the
        following hydrocarbons is bubbled through bromine solution.

    i)
    $$
    \begin{array}{cccc}
    & H & & H \\
    & | & & | \\
    H-C & -C=C & -C-H \\
    & | \; | & \; | & | \\
    & H \; H & \; H & H
    \end{array}
    $$

    ii)
    $$
    \begin{array}{ccccc}
    & H & & & H \\
    & | & & & | \\
    C=C & -C & =C & -C-H \\
    | \; | & \; | & \; | & | \\
    H \; H & \; H & \; H & H
    \end{array}
    $$

    (b) What name is given to the kind of reaction that takes place?

4.

$$\text{chloroethane} \xleftarrow{\text{H}_2} \mathbf{X} \xrightarrow{\mathbf{Y}} \begin{array}{cc} \text{H} & \text{H} \\ | & | \\ \text{H}-\text{C}-\text{C}-\text{H} \\ | & | \\ \text{Cl} & \text{Cl} \end{array}$$

(a) Draw the full structural formula for compound **X**.
(b) Name reagent **Y**.

5. In the commercial production of monochloroethene, the initial stage is the direct chlorination of ethene to form an intermediate compound known as EDC.

ethene + chlorine $\rightarrow$ EDC

The EDC is then purified and converted to monochloroethene and hydrogen chloride by a thermal cracking process.
At certain temperatures, monochloroethene recombines with hydrogen chloride to produce an isomer of EDC.

(a) What type of chemical reaction is involved in the direct chlorination of ethene?
(b) Draw a structural formula for
   i)   monochloroethene,
   ii) the intermediate compound known as EDC,
   iii) the isomer of EDC produced by monochloroethene recombining with hydrogen chloride.

6. Compound **Q** is an unbranched hydrocarbon that reacts as follows.

$$C_6H_{11}Br \xleftarrow{} C_6H_{10} \xrightarrow[\text{heat, pressure}]{\text{H}_2 + \text{nickel catlyst}} C_6H_{12}$$
$$\mathbf{P} \qquad\qquad\qquad \mathbf{Q} \qquad\qquad\qquad \mathbf{R}$$

(a) Given that compound **R** does **not** undergo further addition, draw a structural formula for each of **P**, **Q** and **R**.
(b) What reagent would be used to convert **Q** to **P**?

Alcohols

1. Give the systematic name for each of the following alcohols.

   (a) CH_3-CH_2-OH

   (b) $CH_3-CH-CH_2-CH_3$
       with OH below CH

   (c) $CH_3-CH_2-\overset{\overset{\displaystyle CH_3}{|}}{\underset{\underset{\displaystyle OH}{|}}{C}}-CH_3$

   (d) $CH_3-CH-CH_2-\overset{\overset{\displaystyle CH_3}{|}}{CH}-CH_3$
       with OH below first CH

   (e) $CH_3-CH_2-\overset{\overset{\displaystyle CH_3}{|}}{\underset{\underset{\displaystyle OH}{|}}{C}}-CH_2-CH_3$

   (f) $CH_3-CH-\overset{\overset{\displaystyle CH_3}{|}}{CH}-CH_3$
       with OH below first CH

2. Draw a structural formula for each of the following alcohols.
   (a) butan-1-ol
   (b) 2-methylhexan-3-ol
   (c) 2,3-dimethylpentan-1-ol
   (d) 3,3-dimethylbutan-2-ol

3. Ethane-1,2-diol is a dihydric alcohol used as anti-freeze for car cooling systems.
   (a) Draw the full structural formula for ethane-1,2-diol.
   (b) Suggest what is meant by a dihydric alcohol.

4. Two isomeric straight-chain alcohols, each having four carbon atoms, are known.
   (a) Draw a structural formula for each of these alcohols.
   (b) Draw a structural formula for the isomeric branched-chain alcohol.

5. The addition reaction between steam and ethene is of industrial importance.

$$
\begin{array}{c}
\text{H} \qquad\quad \text{H} \\
\diagdown \qquad \diagup \\
\text{C}=\text{C} \qquad + \quad H_2O \qquad \rightarrow \qquad ? \\
\diagup \qquad \diagdown \\
\text{H} \qquad\quad \text{H}
\end{array}
$$

(a) Name the product of this reaction.
(b) Give another name for this type of reaction.

6. (a) When butan-2-ol is passed over heated aluminium oxide, the elements of water are lost from adjacent carbon atoms and a double bond is formed.

$$
\begin{array}{c}
\text{hot } Al_2O_3 \\
CH_3-CH-CH_2-CH_3 \quad \xrightarrow{} \quad \textbf{A} \quad + \quad \textbf{B} \\
| \quad \text{heat} \\
OH \\
\text{butan-2-ol}
\end{array}
$$

i) Draw a structural formula for each of the isomeric hydrocarbons **A** and **B**.
ii) Suggest a name for the kind of reaction that takes place.
(b) Isomers of pentanol can undergo a similar reaction.
i) Name the **TWO** straight-chain isomers that form **one** product.
ii) Name the straight-chain isomer that forms **two** products.

Carboxylic acids

1. Give the systematic name for each of the following carboxylic acids.

(a)

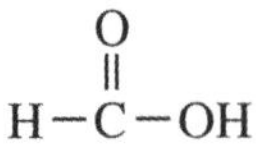

$$H-\overset{\overset{\displaystyle O}{\|}}{C}-OH$$

(b)

$$CH_3-\overset{\overset{\displaystyle CH_3}{|}}{CH}-CH_2-\overset{\overset{\displaystyle O}{\|}}{C}-OH$$

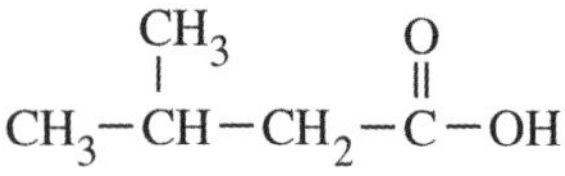

(c)

$$CH_3-CH_2-\overset{\overset{\displaystyle CH_3}{|}}{CH}-CH_2-\overset{\overset{\displaystyle O}{\|}}{C}-OH$$

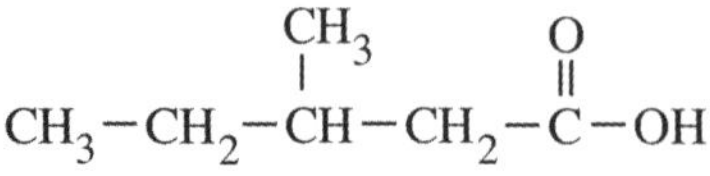

(d)

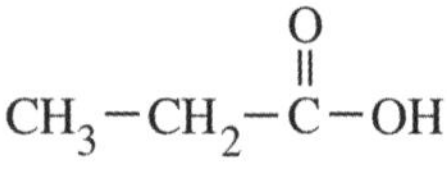

$$CH_3-CH_2-\overset{\overset{\displaystyle O}{\|}}{C}-OH$$

(e)

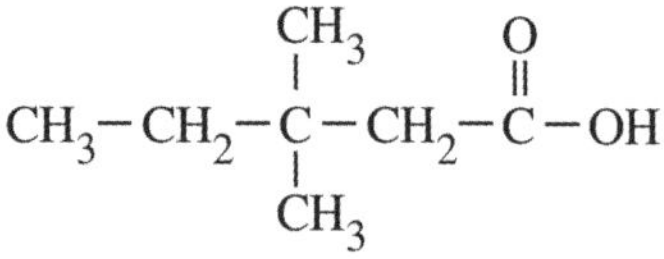

$$CH_3-CH_2-\overset{\overset{\displaystyle CH_3}{|}}{\underset{\underset{\displaystyle CH_3}{|}}{C}}-CH_2-\overset{\overset{\displaystyle O}{\|}}{C}-OH$$

(f)

$$CH_3-\overset{\overset{\displaystyle CH_3}{|}}{CH}-\overset{\overset{\displaystyle CH_3}{|}}{CH}-\overset{\overset{\displaystyle O}{\|}}{C}-OH$$

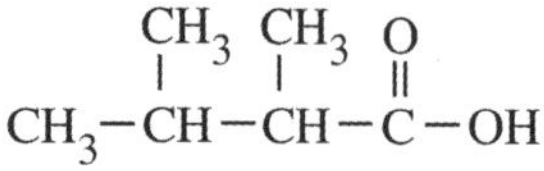

2. Draw a structural formula for each of the following acids.
   (a) ethanoic acid
   (b) 2-methylpentanoic acid
   (c) 4,4-dimethylhexanoic acid

3. (a) Draw a structural formula for butanoic acid.
   (b) Draw a structural formula for an isomeric acid of butanoic acid.

4. For each of the following reactions
   i) write a word equation,
   ii) write a balanced equation.
   (a) magnesium with ethanoic acid
   (b) sodium hydroxide with methanoic acid
   (c) copper(II) oxide with propanoic acid
   (d) potassium carbonate with butanoic acid

Esters (i)

1. Name each of the following esters.

   (a)
   $$CH_3-\overset{\overset{\displaystyle O}{\|}}{C}-O-CH_3$$

   (b)
   $$CH_3-O-\overset{\overset{\displaystyle O}{\|}}{C}-H$$

   (c) $CH_3COOCH_2CH_2CH_3$

   (d) $HCOOCH_2CH_3$

2. Draw a structural formula for each of the following esters.
   (a) ethyl ethanoate   (b)   propyl butanoate

3. Name the ester that is formed from each of the following parent alcohols and carboxylic acids.
   (a) ethanol / methanoic acid   (b)   methanol / propanoic acid
   (c) CH_3CH_2OH / CH_3COOH (d) $CH_3CH_2CH_2OH$ / $HCOOH$

4. Name the products of the breakdown of each of the following esters.
   (a) ethyl propanoate   (b)   methyl ethanoate

   (c)
   $$CH_3CH_2-O-\overset{\overset{\displaystyle O}{\|}}{C}-H$$

   (d)
   $$CH_3CH_2CH_2-\overset{\overset{\displaystyle O}{\|}}{C}-O-CH_3$$

5. A carbon compound has the formula $HCOOCH_3$.
   (a) Name this compound.
   (b) The compound can be broken up on treatment with sodium hydroxide solution.
        Name the **TWO** products of this reaction.

6. The ester opposite can be broken down when warmed with concentrated sulphuric acid.
   Name the **TWO** products of this reaction.

   $$CH_3-\overset{\overset{\displaystyle O}{\|}}{C}-O-\underset{\underset{\displaystyle CH_3}{|}}{CH}-CH_2-CH_3$$

7. (a) Draw a structural formula for the **TWO** esters that are isomers of propanoic acid.
   (b) Name each of the esters.

Esters (ii)

1. Preparation of ethyl ethanoate from ethanoic acid and ethanol results in an equilibrium mixture.

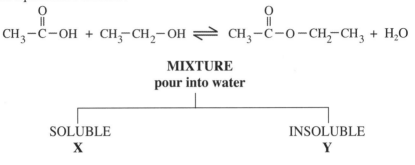

$$CH_3-\overset{\overset{\displaystyle O}{\|}}{C}-OH \; + \; CH_3-CH_2-OH \; \rightleftharpoons \; CH_3-\overset{\overset{\displaystyle O}{\|}}{C}-O-CH_2-CH_3 \; + \; H_2O$$

MIXTURE
pour into water

SOLUBLE   INSOLUBLE
X   **Y**

(a) Name the kind of reaction that takes place in the preparation.

(b) Name the substance(s) present at **X** and **Y**.

2. (a) Salicylic acid occurs in the form of its methyl ester as a constituent of oil of wintergreen.
    The formula for salicylic acid may be represented:

Draw a structural formula for the ester formed when salicylic acid reacts with methanol.

(b) Acetylsalicylic acid is widely used as a pain killer under its commercial name "Aspirin".
The formula may be written as:

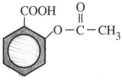

i)   What is meant by hydrolysis?

ii) Draw structural formulae for the products of the hydrolysis of Aspirin.

iii) Suggest why Aspirin tablets which are kept for many months, especially in hot and humid climates, often smell of vinegar (ethanoic acid).

3. The artificial sweetener, aspartame, is a methyl ester of the dipeptide shown.

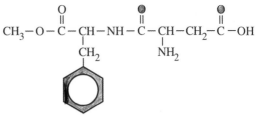

Draw a structural formula for aspartame.

4. Part of a workcard outlining the laboratory preparation of an ester is shown.

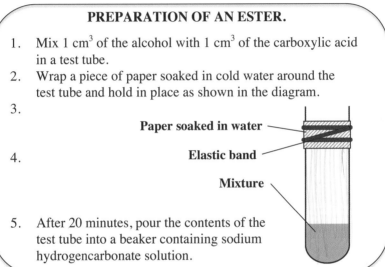

PREPARATION OF AN ESTER.

1. Mix 1 cm^3 of the alcohol with 1 cm^3 of the carboxylic acid in a test tube.
2. Wrap a piece of paper soaked in cold water around the test tube and hold in place as shown in the diagram.
3.

   Paper soaked in water

4.

   Elastic band

   Mixture

5. After 20 minutes, pour the contents of the test tube into a beaker containing sodium hydrogencarbonate solution.

(a) Write down appropriate instructions for Steps 3 and 4 to complete the workcard.
(b) What is the purpose of the paper soaked in water at the mouth of the test tube?
(c) What evidence, apart from smell, shows that a new substance is formed?
(d) Why are the contents of the test tube added to sodium hydrogencarbonate solution rather than just water?

5. (a) Give **TWO** reasons why esters are commonly found in perfumes.
   (b) i) Explain why esters are good solvents for many compounds that are insoluble in water.
       ii) Give **TWO** uses based on this fact.

Fats and oils

1. (a) Give **TWO** reasons why fats and oils can be a useful part of a balanced diet.
   (b) Explain why oils tend to have lower melting points than fats.

2. The structure of an oil can be represented as shown.

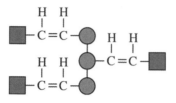

   (a) Draw the structure of the fat that could be produced by "hardening" this oil.
   (b) What is the effect of hardening on the melting point of this oil?
   (c) Name the kind of chemical reaction that takes place during the hardening process.

3. The breakdown of fats produces fatty acids and glycerol.
   (a) Draw a structural formula for glycerol.
   (b) State the ratio of glycerol molecules to fatty acid molecules in the product mixture.

4. A triglyceride breaks up to produce only glycerol and palmitic acid.

$$CH_3-(CH_2)_{14}-\overset{\overset{\displaystyle O}{\|}}{C}-OH \quad \textbf{palmitic acid.}$$

   (a) To which set of compounds do triglycerides belong?
   (b) Draw a structural formula for the triglyceride.
   (c) Explain whether the triglyceride is likely to be a fat or an oil.

5. Mutton fat contains a compound called tristearin.

$$
\begin{array}{l}
H \quad\ \ O \\
| \qquad \| \\
H-C-O-C-C_{17}H_{35} \\
\quad\ | \qquad O \\
\qquad\quad\ \| \\
H-C-O-C-C_{17}H_{35} \\
\quad\ | \qquad O \\
\qquad\quad\ \| \\
H-C-O-C-C_{17}H_{35} \\
\quad\ | \\
\quad\ H
\end{array}
$$

Tristearin is broken down in the body during digestion.
(a) Name the kind of reaction that takes place.
(b) The break down of tristearin produces a fatty acid.
   i) Is the fatty acid saturated or unsaturated?
   ii) Name the other product of this reaction.

6. Two reactions are involved in the making of soaps from fats and oils.
(a) Name the type of reaction that takes place when the fats/oils
    are broken down to produce fatty acids and glycerol.
(b) Name the type of reaction that takes place in the second step.

7. (a) Describe the structure of the compounds that are the main constituents
       of soaps.
(b) Explain the cleansing action of soap on an oil stain.

8. The meaning of the words with the prefix 'hydro' is usually linked with
   water.
   State what is meant by
   (a) hydrophobic,
   (b) hydrophilic.

9. (a) What is meant by hard water?
   (b) What problem is caused with the use of soaps in hard-water areas?
   (c) What is the advantage of using a detergent rather than a soap in hard-
       water areas?

10. When comparing the structure of a soap and a detergent
    (a) state an important similarity,
    (b) state an important difference.

11. Mayonnaise is a stable emulsion of vegetable oil and vinegar with egg yolk.
    (a) What is meant by an emulsion?
    (b) Explain why the emulsifier in egg yolk prevents the oil and vinegar in mayonnaise from separating into layers.

12. Glycerol monostearate is an emulsifier that is used to give ice cream its smooth texture.
    The structure can be represented:

$$CH_2-O-\overset{\displaystyle O}{\overset{\displaystyle \|}{C}}-C_{17}H_{35}$$
$$CH-OH$$
$$CH_2-OH$$

    How does the structure of the compound enable it to act as an emulsifier?

Proteins

1. (a) Give **TWO** reasons why proteins are an essential part of a balanced diet.
   (b) What kind of molecules are formed by the hydrolysis of proteins?
   (c) Name **FOUR** elements found in all proteins.

2. Glycine is an amino acid with the following structure.

$$H-\underset{\underset{H}{|}}{\overset{\overset{H}{|}}{N}}-CH_2-\overset{\overset{O}{||}}{C}-OH$$

   (a) Draw the structure of **three** repeating units in the polymer that would be formed from glycine.
   (b) What kind of reaction would be taking place?
   (c) The body cannot make all the amino acids required for proteins and is dependent on dietary protein for the supply of certain amino acids.
   What name is given to such amino acids?

3. The diagram shows how amino acids are linked together in a protein.

$$-\underset{\underset{H}{|}}{N}-CH_2-\overset{\overset{O}{||}}{C}-\underset{\underset{H}{|}}{N}-\underset{\underset{CH_3}{|}}{\overset{\overset{H}{|}}{C}}-\overset{\overset{O}{||}}{C}-\underset{\underset{H}{|}}{N}-CH_2-\overset{\overset{O}{||}}{C}-\underset{\underset{H}{|}}{N}-\underset{\underset{CH_3}{|}}{\overset{\overset{H}{|}}{C}}-\overset{\overset{O}{||}}{C}-$$

   (a) Draw the structure of the part of the molecule known as the peptide link.
   (b) i) How many different amino acids would be produced in the breakdown of this part of the polymer?
   ii) Draw a structural formula for each of these amino acids.
   iii) What kind of reaction would be taking place?

4. Enzymes are responsible for catalysing most of the reactions that take place in a cell, e.g. the hydrolysis of fats, sugars and proteins.
   (a) To which set of compounds do enzymes belong?
   (b) Use diagrams to describe how an enzyme could catalyse a specific reaction occurring in a cell.

5. The artificial sweetener, aspartame, has the strucure shown.

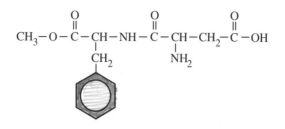

Aspartame's sweetness depends on the shape and structure of the molecule. Two amino acids, aspartic acid and phenylalanine, are formed when it is hydrolysed.
(a) Draw a structural formula for each of the amino acids produced during hydrolysis.
(b) Suggest a reason why aspartame is **not** used in food that will be cooked, but can be used in cold drinks.

6. Maltase is an enzyme that has optimum activity in alkaline conditions.
(a) Why does maltase catalyse the hydrolysis of maltose but **not** the hydrolysis of sucrose?
(b) Why does maltase lose its ability to act as a catalyst in acid conditions?
(c) State another factor that can affect the efficiency of an enzyme.

Plastics and fibres

1. Polymerisation occurs between the following two compounds.

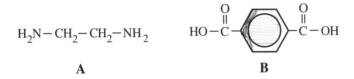

$$H_2N-CH_2-CH_2-NH_2$$

A

B

(a) To which classes of organic compounds do each of **A** and **B** belong?
(b) What type of polymerisation occurs between these two compounds?
(c) Draw the structure of part of the polymer chain showing how **two** of each of the monomer units have joined together.

2. Terylene is a synthetic polymer. It is made from the two monomers shown.

(a) Name the small molecule that is usually a product in a condensation reaction.
(b) Draw the structure of part of the polymer showing how **two** of each of the monomer units have joined together.
(c) What type of polymerisation occurs between these two compounds?

3. The diagram shows part of the structure of a polyester molecule.

(a) Draw the structure of the repeating unit.
(b) Draw a structural formula for the **TWO** monomers used to make the polyester.

4. Caprolactam is an intermediate in the manufacture of nylon.
The structure of caprolactam is:

caprolactam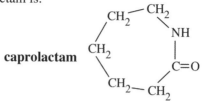

(a) i) In a polymeriser, water reacts with a small percentage of the
caprolactam, opening the ring by hydrolysis and producing
a molecule with two different functional groups.
Draw a structural formula for each of the molecules produced.

ii) This molecule initiates a chain reaction with other caprolactam
molecules. As a result, each ring is opened and the molecules
join head to tail, to form a polymer. This is called nylon 6.
Draw the structure of part of the polymer showing **three**
repeating units.

(b) The structure of nylon 6,6 is:

$$-N-(CH_2)_6-N-C-(CH_2)_4-C-N-(CH_2)_6-N-C-(CH_2)_4-C-$$

i) Draw the structure of the repeating unit of nylon 6,6.

ii) Draw a structural formula for the **TWO** monomers from
which nylon 6,6 is made.

iii) What type of polymer is nylon 6,6?

Carbonyl compounds

1. Give the systematic name for each of the following carbonyl compounds.

(a) $CH_3-CH_2-\underset{\underset{\displaystyle H}{|}}{C}=O$

(b) $CH_3-\overset{\overset{\displaystyle O}{||}}{C}-CH_2-CH_2-CH_3$

(c) $CH_3-\underset{\underset{\displaystyle CH_3}{|}}{CH}-CH_2-\underset{\underset{\displaystyle H}{|}}{C}=O$

(d) $CH_3-\overset{\overset{\displaystyle O}{||}}{C}-CH_2-\underset{\underset{\displaystyle CH_3}{|}}{\overset{\overset{\displaystyle CH_3}{|}}{C}}-CH_3$

(e) $CH_3-\underset{\underset{\displaystyle H}{|}}{C}=O$

(f) $CH_3-CH_2-\overset{\overset{\displaystyle O}{||}}{C}-CH_3$

(g) $CH_3-CH_2-\underset{\underset{\displaystyle H}{|}}{\overset{\overset{\displaystyle CH_3}{|}}{CH}}-C=O$

(h) $CH_3-\underset{\underset{\displaystyle CH_3}{|}}{\overset{\overset{\displaystyle CH_3}{|}}{C}}-CH_2-\overset{\overset{\displaystyle O}{||}}{C}-CH_3$

2. Draw a structural formula for each of the following carbonyl compounds.
    (a) methanal
    (b) propanone
    (c) 3-ethylhexanal
    (d) 3,3-dimethylhexan-2-one

3. Compounds **A** and **B** are straight-chain isomers of pentan-2-one.
    Both also contain a carbonyl group.
    (a) Draw a structural formula for each of the compounds **A** and **B**.
    (b) Name isomers **A** and **B**.

4. (a) Draw a structural formula for propanal.
   (b) To which homologous series does propanal belong?
   (c) i) Does propanal have an isomer that belongs to the same homologous series?
       ii) Explain your answer.
   (d) i) Draw a structural formula for an isomer of propanal that is in a different homologous series.
       ii) To which homologous series does this isomer belong?

5. When ozone, O_3, is bubbled into a solution of a straight-chain alkene, an ozonide is formed. This compound decomposes on treatment with water. The reaction can be represented:

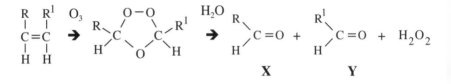

(R and R^1 are hydrogen atoms or alkyl groups.)

   (a) To which homologous series do the substances **X** and **Y** belong?
   (b) i) Give the systematic name for each of the products **X** and **Y** that would be formed if propene was used in the above reaction sequence.
       ii) Name an alkene that would react in this way to give **one** product only.

Primary, secondary and tertiary alcohols

1. State whether each of the following is a primary, secondary or a tertiary alcohol.

    (a) $CH_3-CH_2-CH_2-OH$

    (b)
    $$CH_3-\underset{\underset{OH}{|}}{\overset{\overset{CH_3}{|}}{C}}-CH_2-CH_3$$

    (c)
    $$CH_3-\underset{\underset{OH}{|}}{CH}-\underset{\underset{CH_3}{|}}{\overset{\overset{CH_3}{|}}{C}}-CH_3$$

    (d) CH_3-CH_2-OH

    (e)
    $$HO-CH_2-\underset{\underset{}{}}{\overset{\overset{CH_3}{|}}{CH}}-CH_2-CH_3$$

    (f)
    $$CH_3-\underset{\underset{CH_3}{|}}{\overset{\overset{CH_3}{|}}{C}}-\underset{\underset{OH}{|}}{CH}-CH_3$$

2. State whether each of the following is a primary, secondary or tertiary alcohol.
    (a) butan-2-ol
    (b) pentan-1-ol
    (c) 2-methylbutan-l-ol
    (d) 3,3-dimethylpentan-2-ol
    (e) ethylpentan-3-ol
    (f) 2,3,3-trimethylhexan-2-ol

3. Copy the following carbon skeleton **three** times and add one hydroxyl group to each to make a primary, secondary and tertiary alcohol.

$$
\begin{array}{c}
| \\
-C- \\
| \quad | \quad | \quad | \\
-C-C-C-C- \\
| \quad | \quad | \quad |
\end{array}
$$

Oxidation of carbon compounds

1. Name the type of alcohol
   (a) that can be oxidised to produce an aldehyde,
   (b) that can be oxidised to produce a ketone,
   (c) that **cannot** be oxidised to produce a carbonyl compound.

2. (a) Name **TWO** oxidising agents that can be used to produce a carbonyl compound from an alcohol.
   (b) Describe what is observed in each of the reactions.

3. Name the alcohol that can be used to prepare each of the following carbonyl compounds
   (a) methanal
   (b) butanal
   (c) pentan-2-one
   (d) pentan-3-one

4. Draw a structural formula for the carbonyl compound
   (a) that is formed by the oxidation of hexan-1-ol,
   (b) that is formed by the oxidation of hexan-2-ol.

5. (a) Name **THREE** oxidising agents that can be used to distinguish an aldehyde from a ketone.
   (b) Describe what is observed when the test shows an aldehyde is present.

6.   alcohol **X**   ➔   compound **Y**   ➔
   (a) Name alcohol **X**.
   (b) Draw a structural formula for compound **Y**.

7. C_3H_7OH ➔ C_3H_6O
        A   **B**

Ketone **B** can be obtained from alcohol **A**.
(a) Draw a structural formula for each of **A** and **B**.
(b) Name the type of reaction taking place.

8. Primary alcohols may be oxidised to carboxylic acids in two stages.
(a) Draw a structural formula for each of the products obtained by the oxidation of 2-methylbutan-1-ol.
(b) Name each of the products.

9. What happens to the oxygen to hydrogen ratio in the oxidation of alcohols and aldehydes?

10. An alcohol **X**, on mild oxidation, gives a compound **Y**, of molecular mass 72. Compound **Y** can **not** be oxidised further.
(a) Draw a structural formula for each of **X** and **Y**.
(b) Give the systematic name for alcohol **X**.
(c) Is **X** a primary, secondary or tertiary alcohol?

11.   oxidation
      $C_6H_{12}O$ ➔   cyclohexanone

    compound **A**

(a) Draw a structural formula for cyclohexanone.
(b) Name compound **A**.

12. Butanone can be formed by the catalytic dehydrogenation of butan-2-ol.

              zinc oxide
    butan-2-ol   ➔   butanone   +   hydrogen
              catalyst

(a) Give another name for this type of reaction.
(b) Why does catalytic dehydrogenation **not** occur if the butan-2-ol is replaced by methylpropan-2-ol?

13. Acrolein is a feedstock for the production of useful organic compounds.
    Acrolein can take part in both oxidation and reduction reactions.

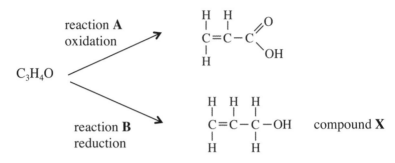

reaction **A**
oxidation

C_3H_4O

reaction **B**
reduction

compound **X**

(a) Draw a structural formula for acrolein.
(b) Why can reaction **B** be classified as reduction?
(c) Compound **X** has an isomer that belongs to a different homologous
    series and has no effect on Benedict's solution.
    Draw a structural formula for this isomer.

14. Butan-l-ol can be converted into compound **X** in two stages.

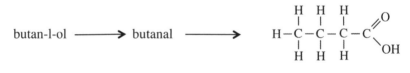

butan-l-ol ⟶ butanal ⟶

compound **X**

(a) Draw a structural formula for
    i)   an isomer of butanal that belongs to the **same** homologous
         series,
    ii) an isomer of butanal that belongs to a **different** homologous
         series.
(b) Name the type of chemical reaction taking place at each of the steps
(c) Name a reagent that could be used to convert butanal to compound **X**.

Miscellaneous reactions

1.

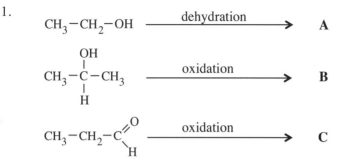

Draw a structural formula for each of the products **A**, **B** and **C**.

2.   Alcohol **A** has the structure:

$$CH_3-\underset{\underset{\displaystyle \text{alcohol } \mathbf{A}}{}}{\overset{\overset{\displaystyle CH_3 \quad OH}{|\quad\quad|}}{CH-CH}}-CH_3$$

(a)   Alcohol **A** is passed over hot copper(II) oxide.
     Which class of organic compound is formed?

(b)   i)   Alcohol **A** can react with the loss of water to produce two
          isomeric alkenes.

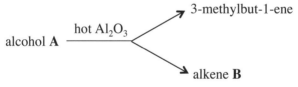

     Draw a structural formula for alkene **B**.

     ii)   Draw a structural formula for the compound formed when
          3-methylbut-1-ene reacts with chlorine.

3.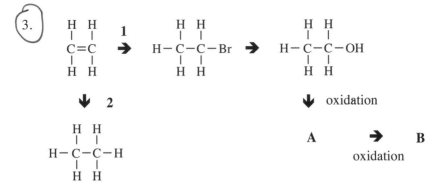

(a) i) Draw the full structural formula for each of the compounds **A** and **B**.

   ii) Name a reagent that would bring about the reaction of **A** to produce **B**.

(b) Name the reagents in each of steps **1** and **2**.

4. An unknown liquid, formula C_3H_6O, is involved in the tests shown.

Test	Reagent	Observation
A	Bromine water	No reaction
B	2,4 DNP (test for carbonyl group)	orange precipitate (positive result)
C	Benedict's solution	No reaction

(a) State what can be deduced about the structure of the liquid from
   i)   test **A**,
   ii) tests **B** and **C** together.

(b) Name the liquid and draw its full structural formula.

5. Propanone is a widely used solvent. It can be made from propene in **two** steps.
   Using structural formulae show each of the steps involved in this preparation and name the reagents used in each step.

6.

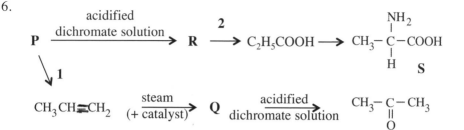

The reaction scheme shows a number of common reactions.
(a) Name each of compounds **P** and **Q**.
(b) Draw a structural formula for compound **R**.
(c) Name the **TWO** functional groups in compound **S**.
(d) Name each of the types of reaction occurring at steps **1** and **2**.

7. There are four isomeric alcohols of molecular formula C_4H_9OH.
Their structural formulae are as follows.

$CH_3-CH_2-CH_2-CH_2-OH$

(I)

$CH_3-CH_2-CH-CH_3$
            |
            OH   (II)

$CH_3-\underset{\underset{CH_3}{|}}{\overset{\overset{CH_3}{|}}{C}}-OH$ (III)

$CH_3-\underset{\underset{CH_3}{|}}{CH}-CH_2-OH$ (IV)

(a) i) Give a systematic name for each of compounds (I), (II), (III) and (IV).
    ii) State which of the compounds (I) to (IV) are primary, which secondary and which tertiary alcohols.
(b) The four alcohols are contained separately in four bottles marked **A**, **B**, **C** and **D**.
    From the following information decide which bottle contains which alcohol. State your reason briefly at each stage.
    i) The contents of **A**, **B** and **C** can be readily oxidised by acidified potassium dichromate solution, while those of **D** cannot.
    ii) **A** and **B** on complete oxidation by acidified dichromate solution give acids of formulae C_3H_7COOH; **C** does not give this acid.
    iii) All four substances can be dehydrated to give alkenes.
        A and **D** can both form the same alkene.
        B and **C** can both form the same alkene, which is an isomer of that formed by **A** and **D**.

8. A gaseous compound **X** is known to be an alkene with a molecular formula of C_4H_8.

(a) i)   Draw structural formulae for **TWO** straight-chain alkenes and **ONE** branched-chain alkene having this molecular formula.

   ii) Name each of the isomers.

(b) The position of the double bond in an alkene may be determined by a process called ozonolysis, in which the alkene is split (by ozone) at the double bond to give two carbonyl compounds.

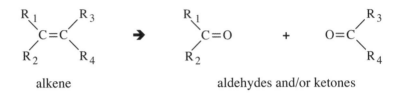

alkene   aldehydes and/or ketones

(R_1, R_2, R_3 and R_4 are hydrogen atoms or alkyl groups.)

When the numbers and arrangements of carbon atoms in the products are known, the position of the double bond in the original alkene, and hence its structure, may be determined.

On ozonolysis, alkene **X** formed two compounds **Y** and **Z**.
Only **Y** gave a positive test with Benedict's solution.

i)   What would be seen to indicate a positive result in the Benedict's test?

ii) What do the actual test results indicate about the structures of carbonyl compounds **Y** and **Z**?

iii) From the information above, deduce which of the isomers referred to in (a) is alkene **X**.

(c) A further isomer of alkene **X** belongs to a different homologous series from those referred to in (a).

i)   Draw its structural formula.

ii) Give its systematic name.

iii) Describe a test which would distinguish this isomer from the others.

9.

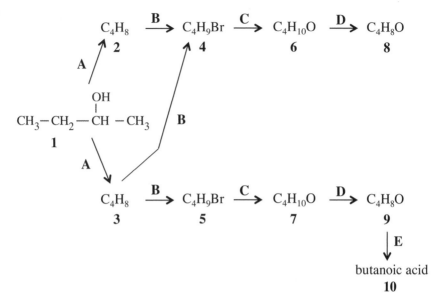

(a) Is compound **1** a primary, secondary or tertiary alcohol?
(b) Draw a structural formula for each of the isomeric compounds **2** and **3**.
(c) Name the type of reaction taking place in each of steps **A** and **B**.
(d) Name a reagent that could be used in each of steps **D** and **E**.
(e) Draw a structural formula for each of the isomeric compounds **8** and **9**.
(f) Which of compounds **6** and **7** is an isomer of compound **1**?

Everyday chemistry

1. Both vanillin and eugenol have distinctive flavours.

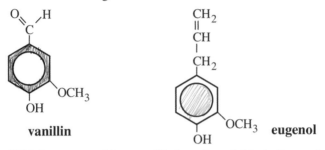

vanillin

eugenol

(a) Which compound is more likely to be soluble in fats and oils?
(b) Explain your answer.

2. Limonene is a monoterpene that can be extracted from the peel of lemons and oranges. It is more volatile than squalene, a triterpene with the molecular formula $C_{30}H_{50}$.

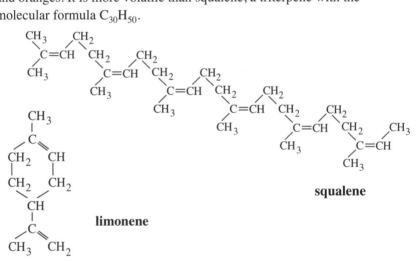

limonene

squalene

(a) i) What is meant by a volatile compound?
    ii) Explain why limonene evaporates more easily than squalene.
(b) Limonene is increasingly being used as a solvent for cleaning purposes, such as the removal of oil from machine parts.
    Explain why limonene is a good solvent for machine oil.

3. Camphor is a carbonyl compound with the molecular formula, $C_{10}H_{16}O$.

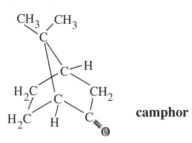

camphor

(a) Which would be a better solvent for camphor, water or acetone?
(b) Explain your answer.

4. Covalent compounds are generally insoluble in water.
    Fructose is one of the exceptions.

$$
\begin{array}{l}
CH_2OH \\
| \\
C=O \\
| \\
CHOH \\
| \\
CHOH \\
| \\
CHOH \\
| \\
CH_2OH
\end{array}
$$

fructose

Explain why fructose is very soluble in water.

5. The 'flavour compounds' in asparagus have polar groups; the 'flavour compounds' in green peas do **not** have polar groups.
    (a) Which vegetable should be cooked in oils/butter to retain the flavour?
    (b) Explain your answer.

6. (a) What is meant by an essential oil?
    (b) The following plants are sources of essential oils.

    basil, eucalyptus, grapefruit, juniper, lavender, lemon, orange, rose, thyme, wintergreen

    Copy and complete the table below to show the part of each of the above plants that is the source of the essential oil.

Peel	Berry	Leaf	Flower

7. (a) What is the collective name for the family of carbon compounds formed by the joining of isoprene units?
   (b) Choose **TWO** terms from the following list that can be used to describe the structure of isoprene.

   aldehyde , ester, hydrocarbon, ketone, saturated, unsaturated

8. Myrcene and selinene are compounds formed by joining together isoprene units.

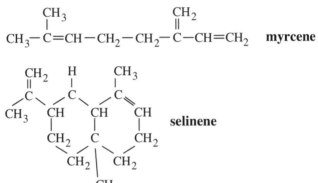

   (a) Explain what happens when selinene is added to bromine solution.
   (b) i) Copy the structure of myrcene and circle a group of atoms to show **one** isoprene unit.
   (b) ii) How many isoprene units are used in the making of **one** selinene molecule?

9. Give **TWO** examples of the deterioration of food quality that can result from the oxidation of food molecules.

10. (a) Why are crisps packaged in nitrogen?
    (b) Why are cucumbers sealed in cellophane or coated in wax?

11. (a) What is meant by an antioxidant?
    (b) Why are they added to foods?
    (c) What happens to an antioxidant in any reaction that takes place?

Free radicals

1. (a) What is meant by a free radical?
    (b) Why are free radicals formed in the atmosphere?

2. Sun-block products limit the damage to the skin caused by photoaging.
    (a) What is the cause of photoaging?
    (b) Why does the use of sun-block products limit the damage to the skin when in the sun?

3. The different forms of vitamin E are all free radical scavengers that can occur naturally. All forms have a hydroxyl group that can release hydrogen atoms, $H^\bullet$.
    (a) What is meant by a free radical scavenger?
    (b) Why can the different forms of vitamin E be described as free radical scavengers?

4. (a) What is meant by a free radical chain reaction?
    (b) i)   Name the **THREE** steps that occur in a free radical chain reaction.
        ii) What happens in each step?

5. Hexane decolourises bromine faster in the light than in the dark.
    The following are steps in the free radical chain reaction that occurs.

A	Br_2		$\rightarrow$	$Br^\bullet$	$+$	$Br^\bullet$
B	$Br^\bullet$	$+$ C_6H_{14}	$\rightarrow$	$C_6H_{13}^\bullet$	$+$	HBr
C	$C_6H_{13}^\bullet$	$+$ Br_2	$\rightarrow$	$C_6H_{13}Br$	$+$	$Br^\bullet$
D	$Br^\bullet$	$+$ $Br^\bullet$	$\rightarrow$	Br_2		
E	$Br^\bullet$	$+$ $C_6H_{13}^\bullet$	$\rightarrow$	$C_6H_{13}Br$		
F	$C_6H_{13}^\bullet$	$+$ $C_6H_{13}^\bullet$	$\rightarrow$	$C_{12}H_{26}$		

    Copy and complete the table by placing the letter for each of the equations in the correct column.

Initiation step(s)	Propagation step(s)	Termination step(s)

6. Hydrogen reacts with chlorine in a free radical chain reaction. The reaction is initiated when light energy results in the formation of chlorine free radicals.

   (a) Write an equation for the initiation step.

   (b) Copy and complete the equation below for one of the propagation steps.

$$H^{\cdot} \quad + \quad Cl_2 \quad \rightarrow$$

   (c) Write an equation for **ONE** of the possible termination steps.

Problem solving: patterns in carbon compounds

1. Markovnikoff's Rule

    Addition of hydrogen chloride to an alkene can give two products. Markovnikoff observed that the hydrogen of the hydrogen chloride mainly attaches to the carbon atom of the double bond that already has the most hydrogens directly attached to it.

    (a) Draw the full structural formula for the major product formed when hydrogen chloride reacts with propene.

    (b) Why is it **not** necessary to consider Markovnikoff's rule when hydrogen chloride reacts with but-2-ene?

2. Pyrolysis (thermal decomposition) of esters can produce two compounds, an alkene and a carboxylic acid, according to the following reaction.

    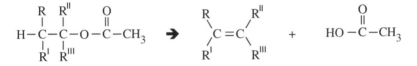

    (R, R^I, R^{II} and R^{III} represent hydrogen atoms or alkyl groups.)

    (a) Name each of the products of thermal decomposition of propyl ethanoate.

    (b) Draw a structural formula for the ester that would produce 2-methylbut-1-ene and ethanoic acid on pyrolysis.

    (c) An ester produced a mixture of **two** different alkenes on pyrolysis. Suggest why this can happen.

    (d) Different carboxylic acids can also be produced on pyrolysis. Name the ester that would produce ethene and methanoic acid.

3. Alcohols can be prepared by the reaction of carbonyl compounds with methyl magnesium bromide. The reaction takes place in two stages.

Stage 1
Methyl magnesium bromide reacts with the carbonyl compound in an addition reaction across the carbonyl group.

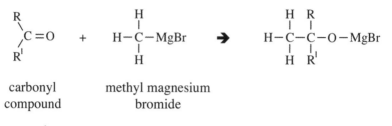

      carbonyl   methyl magnesium
      compound   bromide

(R and R' represent hydrogen atoms or alkyl groups.)

Stage 2
Reaction of the product with water produces the alcohol.

$$H-\overset{\overset{\displaystyle H}{|}}{\underset{\underset{\displaystyle H}{|}}{C}}-\overset{\overset{\displaystyle R}{|}}{\underset{\underset{\displaystyle R'}{|}}{C}}-O-MgBr \;+\; H_2O \;\rightarrow\; H-\overset{\overset{\displaystyle H}{|}}{\underset{\underset{\displaystyle H}{|}}{C}}-\overset{\overset{\displaystyle R}{|}}{\underset{\underset{\displaystyle R'}{|}}{C}}-OH \;+\; MgBrOH$$

                                                             alcohol

(a) i) Draw a structural formula for the alcohol if methanal had been used in this reaction.
   ii) Name the alcohol produced if propanone had been used in this reaction.
  iii) Name the carbonyl compound that would produce 2-methylbutan-2-ol in this reaction.
(b) Suggest a name for the type of reaction that takes place in stage 2.

4. The compound diazomethane, CH_2N_2, undergoes an unusual reaction called **insertion**. Under certain experimental conditions, the CH_2 group produced can insert itself into **any** bond that includes an atom of hydrogen.

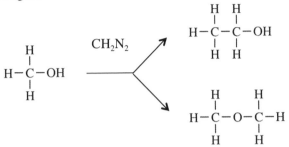

Nitrogen is a product in every reaction.

Draw a structural formula for the **THREE** organic products formed when diazomethane reacts with ethanol.

5. Amines can be produced by reacting ammonia with a carbonyl compound. The reaction, an example of reductive amination, occurs in two stages.

Stage 1 Amination

$$CH_3-\overset{\displaystyle O}{\overset{\displaystyle \|}{C}}-CH_3 \quad + \quad NH_3 \quad \rightarrow \quad CH_3-\overset{\displaystyle \overset{\textstyle H}{|}}{\underset{}{\overset{\displaystyle N}{\|}}}-CH_3$$

Stage 2 Reduction

$$CH_3-\overset{\displaystyle \overset{\textstyle NH_2}{|}}{\underset{\underset{\textstyle H}{|}}{C}}-CH_3 \quad \rightarrow \quad CH_3-\overset{\displaystyle \overset{\textstyle NH_2}{|}}{\underset{\underset{\textstyle H}{|}}{C}}-CH_3$$

(a) i) Name the carbonyl compound that would produce:

$$CH_3-CH_2-CH_2-\overset{\displaystyle \overset{\textstyle NH_2}{|}}{\underset{\underset{\textstyle H}{|}}{C}}-CH_3$$

ii) Draw a structural formula for the amine produced when butanal undergoes reductive amination with ammonia.

(b) Give another name for the type of reaction taking place in Stage 2.

6. Alkenes can react with oxygen to produce unstable compounds called peroxides. These peroxides break down rapidly to form two carbonyl compounds.

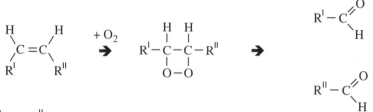

(R^I and R^{II} represent different alkyl groups.)

(a) In one reaction, alkene **X** reacts to produce the two compounds shown.

Name alkene **X** for this reaction.

(b) Name an alkene that would react to produce only **one** carbonyl compound.

7. Aldehydes and ketones can take part in a reaction known as an aldol condensation.

The simplest aldol condensation involves two molecules of ethanal.

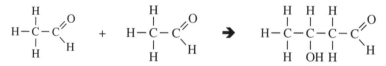

In this reaction, the carbon atom next to the carbonyl functional group of one molecule forms a bond with the carbonyl carbon atom of the second molecule.

(a) Draw a structural formula for the product formed when propanone is used instead of ethanal in this reaction.

(b) Name an aldehyde that would **not** take part in an aldol condensation.

(c) Apart from the structure of the reactants, suggest what is unusual about applying the term "condensation" to this particular type of reaction.

Nature's Chemistry

The design of an industrial process

1. (a) In the chemical industry, what is meant by a feedstock?
   (b) State **THREE** factors that are important in deciding which feedstock to use.

2. Consider the following list.

   sulphuric acid, methane, calcium carbonate, water, hydrogen, sodium chloride, ethene, oxygen, ammonia, nitrogen, potassium hydroxide

   Which of the above can be classified as (relatively) cheap and readily available?

3. (a) What is meant by the sustainability of a feedstock?
   (b) Give an example of a feedstock that can be classified as being sustainable.

4. Give an example of an industrial process in which recycling reduces the waste of unused reactants.

5. The cost of energy is of major importance to the chemical industry. Give a way of keeping down energy costs.

6. In the chemical industry, what is meant by a marketable by-product? Give **TWO** examples of a marketable by-product.

7. In the Haber Process, increasing the pressure increases the yield of the product (ammonia). Why then is the process carried out at 200 atmospheres rather than at a higher pressure?

8. Give **FOUR** examples of steps taken by the chemical industry to reduce damage to the environment.

Mole calculations (revision)

1. Calculate the mass of each of the following compounds.
    (a) 10 mol of CH_4
    (b) 0.5 mol of SO_2
    (c) 2 mol of $CaCO_3$
    (d) 0.1 mol of $(NH_4)_2Cr_2O_7$

2. Calculate the amount, in moles, in each of the following compounds.
    (a) 14 g of C_2H_4
    (b) 202.2 g of KNO_3
    (c) 10.6 g of Na_2CO_3
    (d) 2.642 kg of $(NH_4)_2SO_4$

3. Calculate the amount, in moles, that must be dissolved to make each of the following solutions.
    (a) 200 cm^3 of 1 mol 1^{-1}
    (b) 500 cm^3 of 0.5 mol 1^{-1}
    (c) 100 cm^3 of 2 mol 1^{-1}
    (d) 2 litres of 0.2 mol 1^{-1}

4. Calculate the concentration of each of the following solutions.
    (a) 1 mol of solute dissolved in 500 cm^3 of solution
    (b) 2 mol of solute dissolved in 200 cm^3 of solution
    (c) 0.5 mol of solute dissolved in 250 cm^3 of solution
    (d) 0.1 mol of solute dissolved in 1 litre of solution

5. Calculate the volume of each of the following solutions.
    (a) 1 mol 1^{-1} solution containing 2 mol of solute
    (b) 2 mol 1^{-1} solution containing 0.4 mol of solute
    (c) 0.2 mol 1^{-1} solution containing 0.1 mol of solute
    (d) 1 mol 1^{-1} 1 solution containing 0.2 mol of solute

6. Calculate the mass of substance required to make up each of the following solutions.
   (a) 50 cm^3 of 4 mol l^{-1} KCl (aq)
   (b) 100 cm^3 of 0.2 mol l^{-1} Na$_2$SO$_4$ (aq)
   (c) 25 cm^3 of 1 mol l^{-1} Mg(NO$_3$)$_2$ (aq)
   (d) 500 cm^3 of 0.1 mol l^{-1} (NH$_4$)$_2$CO$_3$ (aq)

7. Calculate the concentration of each of the following solutions.
   (a) 4 g of NaOH dissolved and made up to 1 litre of solution
   (b) 13.82 g of K$_2$CO$_3$ dissolved and made up to 2 litres of solution
   (c) 31.92 g of CuSO$_4$ dissolved and made up to 250 cm^3 of solution
   (d) 10 g of NH$_4$NO$_3$ dissolved and made up to 100 cm^3 of solution

The Avogadro constant (i)

1. Calculate the amount of atoms, in moles, in each of the following compounds.
   (a) oxygen atoms in 0.5 mol of SO_2
   (b) hydrogen atoms in 2 mol of CH_4
   (c) carbon atoms in 4 mol of C_4H_{10}
   (d) atoms in 0.2 mol of NH_3
   (e) atoms in 10 mol of C_2H_5OH

2. Calculate the amount of ions, in moles, in each of the following compounds.
   (a) magnesium ions in 1 mol of Mg_3N_2
   (b) sodium ions in 0.05 mol of Na_2O
   (c) hydroxide ions in 0.1 mol of $Ca(OH)_2$
   (d) ions in 5 mol of $CuSO_4$
   (e) ions in 0.4 mol of NH_4Cl

3. (a) Which contains more atoms, 6 g of magnesium or 6 g of calcium?
   (b) Which contains more atoms, 3 g of sodium or 5 g of potassium?
   (c) Which contains more atoms, 2 g of helium or 10 g of argon?
   (d) Which contains more molecules, 20 g of water
       or 20 g of carbon dioxide?
   (e) Which contains more molecules, 10 g of ammonia or 16 g of oxygen?
   (f) Which contains more molecules, 100 g of methane, CH_4,
       or 50 g of ethane, C_2H_6?
   (g) Which contains more ions, 1 g of lithium chloride
       or 1 g of potassium chloride?
   (h) Which contains more ions, 10 g of magnesium sulphide
       or 2 g of calcium oxide?
   (i) Which contains more ions, 80 g of sodium hydroxide
       or 200 g of sodium sulphate?
   (j) Which contains more atoms, 40 g of neon or 60 g of sulphur dioxide?
   (k) Which contains more atoms, 1 g of hydrogen
       or 50 g of carbon tetrachloride?
   (l) Which contains more atoms, 80 g of hydrogen chloride
       or 10 g of propene, C_3H_6?

The Avogadro constant (ii)
(See note to teachers/students.)

For the questions in this exercise take the Avogadro Constant to be 6.02×10^{23} mol^{-1}.

1. Calculate the number of atoms in each of the following elements.
   - (a) 160.5 g of sulphur
   - (b) 401 g of calcium
   - (c) 0.0014 g of carbon-14
   - (d) 46 kg of sodium

2. Calculate the number of molecules in each of the following compounds.
   - (a) 1.1 g of CO_2
   - (b) 90 g of H_2O
   - (c) 3.2 g of CH_4
   - (d) 3.42 g of $C_{12}H_{22}O_{11}$

3. Calculate the number of formula units in each of the following compounds.
   - (a) 5.81 g of KF
   - (b) 561 g of CaO
   - (c) 269 g of $CuCl_2$
   - (d) 1 kg of NaOH

4. Calculate the number of atoms in each of the following compounds.
   - (a) 1.8 g of H_2O
   - (b) 8.6 g of C_6H_{14}
   - (c) 3.4 g of NH_3
   - (d) 9.2 g of C_2H_5OH

5. Calculate the number of ions in each of the following compounds.
   - (a) 9.42 g of K_2O
   - (b) 1482 g of $Ca(OH)_2$
   - (c) 585 g of NaCl
   - (d) 34.23 kg of $Al_2(SO_4)_3$

6. Calculate the number of electrons lost when one mole of aluminium atoms reacts with dilute nitric acid to form one mole of aluminium ions.

Molar volume of gases

1. Calculate the mass of each of the following gases.

    (Take the molar volume to be 22.4 litres mol^{-1}.)

    (a) 2 litres of argon
    (b) 0.1 litres of methane
    (c) 5 litres of chlorine
    (d) 10 litres of carbon dioxide
    (e) 0.5 litres of oxygen

2. Calculate the volume occupied by each of the following compounds.

    (Take the molar volume to be 24.0 litres mol^{-1}.)

    (a) 0.3 g of ethane
    (b) 0.641 g of sulphur dioxide
    (c) 4.04 g of neon
    (d) 0.76 of fluorine
    (e) 6.8 kg of ammonia

3. Calculate the molar volume of each of the following gases
    (at the particular temperature and pressure).
    (a) 0.226 mol of butane in a 5 litre flask
    (b) 1.12×10^{-2} mol of sulphur dioxide in a 250 cm^3 flask
    (c) 0.38 g of ammonia in a 500 cm^3 flask
    (d) 1.8×10^{-2} g of helium in a 100 cm^3 flask
    (e) 0.174 g of hydrogen in a 2 litre flask

4. A student carried out the following measurements to find the molar volume
    of carbon dioxide.

    Weight of empty flask = 367.30 g
    Weight of flask + carbon dioxide = 368.28 g
    Volume of flask = 500 cm^3

    Calculate the molar volume of carbon dioxide
    (at the particular temperature and pressure).

Calculations based on equations (i) (revision)

1. (a) CH_4 + $2O_2$ ➔ CO_2 + $2H_2O$

    Calculate the mass of carbon dioxide that is produced on burning
    4 g of methane in excess oxygen.

    (b) Cu + $2AgNO_3$ ➔ $Cu(NO_3)_2$ + $2Ag$

    Calculate the mass of silver that is produced when 12.7 g of copper is
    added to excess silver nitrate solution.

    (c) $4Al$ + $3O_2$ ➔ $2Al_2O_3$

    Calculate the mass of aluminium that is required to produce
    10.2 g of aluminium oxide.

    (d) $2NaHCO_3$ ➔ Na_2CO_3 + H_2O + CO_2

    Calculate the mass of carbon dioxide that is produced from
    4.2 g of sodium hydrogencarbonate.

    (e) $(NH_4)_2SO_4$ + $2NaOH$ ➔ Na_2SO_4 + $2NH_3$ + $2H_2O$

    Calculate the mass of ammonium sulphate required to produce
    0.68 g of ammonia.

    (f) C_2H_4 + H_2O ➔ C_2H_5OH

    Calculate the mass of ethanol that is produced from 2.8×10^3 kg of ethene.

    (g) N_2 + $3H_2$ ➔ $2NH_3$

    Calculate the mass of ammonia that is produced from
    6 tonnes of hydrogen.

    (h) $CH_3CH_2CH_2OH$ ➔ CH_3CH_2COOH

    Calculate the mass of propan-1-ol that is required to produce
    1.48 kg of propanoic acid.

2. (a) $Zn\,(s)$ + $H_2SO_4\,(aq)$ → $ZnSO_4\,(aq)$ + $H_2\,(g)$

Calculate the mass of zinc that would react with 25 cm^3 of sulphuric acid, concentration 1 mol l^{-1}.

(b) $Fe\,(s)$ + $2HCl\,(aq)$ → $FeCl_2\,(aq)$ + $H_2\,(g)$

Calculate the mass of iron that would react with 50 cm^3 of hydrochloric acid, concentration 0.1 mol l^{-1}.

(c) $Zn\,(s)$ + $CuSO_4\,(aq)$ → $ZnSO_4\,(aq)$ + $Cu\,(s)$

Calculate the mass of copper produced when excess zinc is added to 50 cm^3 of copper(II) sulphate, concentration 0.5 mol l^{-1}.

3. A student added 12 g of magnesium to 100 cm^3 hydrochloric acid, concentration 0.1 mol l^{-1}.

Calculate the mass of magnesium that would remain at the end of the reaction.

4. A chemist was investigating the mass of calcium carbonate present in different egg shells.
It was found that the calcium carbonate in one of the egg shell samples reacted with 50.10 cm^3 of hydrochloric acid, concentration 1 mol l^{-1}.

Calculate the mass of calcium carbonate present in the egg shell sample.

Calculations based on equations (ii)

For the questions in this exercise take the molar volume of the gases to be 23.2 litres mol^{-1}.

1.   Zn (s)   +   2HCl (aq)   → $ZnCl_2$ (aq)   + H_2 (g)

   Calculate the volume of hydrogen gas that is produced when 6.54 g of zinc is added to excess dilute hydrochloric acid.

2.   S (s)   + O_2 (g)   → SO_2 (g)

   Calculate the volume of oxygen that is required to completely burn 6.42 g of sulphur.

3. $2Ag_2O$ (s)   →   4Ag (s)   + O_2 (g)

   Calculate the volume of oxygen that is produced when 46.36 g of silver oxide completely decomposes.

4. $2H_2$ (g)   + O_2 (g)   → $2H_2O$ (l)

   Calculate the mass of water that is produced when 2 litres of hydrogen is burned in excess oxygen.

5. $2H_2O_2$ (aq)   → $2H_2O$ (l)   + O_2 (g)

   Calculate the mass of hydrogen peroxide that is required to give 58 cm^3 of oxygen.

6. Chlorine is produced in industry by the electrolysis of sodium chloride solution.

   Calculate the volume of chlorine that would be produced from 100 kg of sodium chloride.

7. The first stage in the extraction of copper from sulphide ores such as chalcopyrite ($CuFeS_2$) involves heating the ore with sand and oxygen.

$4CuFeS_2 (s) + 2SiO_2 (s) + 5O_2 (g)$
$\rightarrow 2Cu_2S.FeS (l) + 2FeSiO_2 (l) + 4SO_2 (g)$

Calculate the volume of oxygen that is required to react completely with 1468 kg of chalcopyrite.

8. Hydrogen can be obtained by the reforming of hexane.

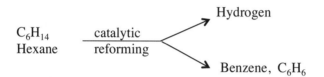

C_6H_{14} catalytic
Hexane   reforming

Hydrogen

Benzene, C_6H_6

Calculate the volume of hydrogen that would be produced when 1 kg of hexane is reformed.

9. $Mg (s) + H_2SO_4 (aq) \rightarrow MgSO_4 (aq) + H_2 (g)$

Calculate the volume of hydrogen gas that is produced when excess magnesium is added to 50 cm^3 of sulphuric acid, concentration 0.1 mol l^{-1}.

10. $Zn (s) + 2HCl (aq) \rightarrow ZnCl_2 (aq) + H_2 (g)$

Calculate the volume of hydrogen gas that is produced when excess zinc is added to 25 cm^3 of hydrochloric acid, concentration 0.5 mol l^{-1}.

11. The burning of propane is an exothermic reaction.

$C_3H_8 (g) + 5O_2 (g) \rightarrow 3CO_2 (g) + 4H_2O (l)$ $\Delta H = 2878$ kJ mol^{-1}

Calculate the volume of propane required to produce 7.195 kJ when burned in excess oxygen.

The idea of excess

1. $C(s) + O_2(g) \rightarrow CO_2(g)$

   Calculate the mass of carbon dioxide that is obtained when 4 g of carbon is burned in 8 g of oxygen.

2. $Fe(s) + S(s) \rightarrow FeS(s)$

   Calculate the mass of iron sulphide that is obtained when 27.9 g of iron is heated with 3.21 g of sulphur.

3. $2H_2(g) + O_2(g) \rightarrow 2H_2O(l)$

   Calculate the mass of water that is obtained when 0.1 mol of hydrogen is ignited with 0.1 mol of oxygen.

4. $2Ca(s) + O_2(g) \rightarrow 2CaO(s)$

   Calculate the mass of calcium oxide that is obtained when 30 g of calcium is burned in 0.25 mol of oxygen.

5. $(NH_4)_2SO_4 + 2NaOH \rightarrow 2NH_3 + Na_2SO_4 + 2H_2O$

   Calculate the mass of ammonia gas that is produced when 1.321 g of ammonium sulphate is heated with 0.5 g of sodium hydroxide.

6. Calculate the mass of magnesium oxide that is obtained when 2.43 g of magnesium is ignited in 10 litres of oxygen.

7. When vitamin C ($C_6H_8O_6$) reacts with iodine solution, the iodine solution is decolourised.

   $$C_6H_8O_6(aq) + I_2(aq) \rightarrow C_6H_6O_6(aq) + 2H^+(aq) + 2I^-(aq)$$
   $$\text{(brown)} \qquad\qquad\qquad\qquad \text{(colourless)}$$

   An iodine solution containing 10 g of iodine is added to 100 cm³ of vitamin C solution, concentration 0.5 mol l⁻¹.
   By calculating which reactant is in excess, state whether the iodine solution would have been decolourised.

In questions 8 and 9 take the molar volume of the gases to be 23.2 litres mol^{-1}.

8. In each of the following reactions, decide by calculation which reactant is in excess, and hence calculate the volume of hydrogen that is produced.

(a) Zn (s) + H_2SO_4 (aq) ➔ $ZnSO_4$ (aq) + H_2 (g)

6.54 g of zinc added to 25 cm^3 of dilute sulphuric acid, concentration 2 mol l^{-1}.

(b) Mg (s) + 2HCl (aq) ➔ $MgCl_2$ (aq) + H_2 (g)

2.43 g of magnesium added to 100 cm^3 of dilute hydrochloric acid, concentration 1 mol l^{-1}.

(c) Fe (s) + 2HCl (aq) ➔ $FeCl_2$ (aq) + H_2 (g)

2.79 g of iron added to 80 cm^3 of dilute hydrochloric acid, concentration 0.5 mol l^{-1}.

(d) Mg (s) + H_2SO_4 (aq) ➔ $MgSO_4$ (aq) + H_2 (g)

0.486 g of magnesium added to 25 cm^3 of dilute sulphuric acid, concentration 1 mol l^{-1}.

9. Na_2SO_3 (s) + 2HCl (aq) ➔ 2NaCl (aq) + H_2O (1) + SO_2 (g)

Calculate the volume of sulphur dioxide that is produced when 1.261 g of sodium sulphite is added to 50 cm^3 of dilute hydrochloric acid, concentration 2 mol l^{-1}.

10. Calcium carbonate reacts with nitric acid.

$CaCO_3$ (s) + 2HNO$_3$ (aq) ➔ Ca(NO$_3$)$_2$ (aq) + H_2O (1) + CO_2 (g)

A 5 g lump of calcium carbonate was added to 100 cm^3 of 0.1 mol l^{-1} nitric acid.

Calculate the mass of calcium carbonate that did not react.

Calculations based on equations (iii)

In this exercise assume that all measurements are made at room temperature and atmospheric pressure, i.e. the same conditions of temperature and pressure.

1. In each of the following reactions calculate the ratio of the volume of product(s) to the volume of reactant(s)

    (a) H_2 (g)   + Cl_2 (g)   → $2HCl$ (g)

    (b) N_2 (g)   + $3H_2$ (g)   → $2NH_3$ (g)

    (c) $2C$ (s)   + O_2 (g)   → $2CO$ (g)

    (d) C_2H_4 (g)   + $3O_2$ (g)   → $2CO_2$ (g)   + $2H_2O$ (l)

    (e) CuO (s)   + CO (g)   → Cu (s)   + CO_2 (g)

2. N_2 (g)   + $2O_2$ (g)   → $2NO_2$ (g)

    Calculate the volume of nitrogen dioxide that is produced when 100 cm^3 of nitrogen is sparked in 150 cm^3 oxygen.

3. The balanced equation for the complete combustion of diphosphine, P_2H_4, is:

    $2P_2H_4$ (g)   + $7O_2$ (g)   → P_4O_{10} (s)   + $4H_2O$ (l)

    10 cm^3 of diphosphine was ignited with 50 cm^3 of oxygen and the remaining gases allowed to cool to room temperature.

    Calculate the volume of unreacted oxygen.

4. When each of the following volumes of gases is burned completely, calculate   i)   the volume of oxygen required,
                            ii)   the volume of carbon dioxide produced.

    (a) 100 cm^3 methane

    (b) 2 litres carbon monoxide

    (c) 250 cm^3 ethene

    (d) 150 cm^3 butane

5. C_3H_8 (g)   + $5O_2$ (g)   → $3CO_2$ (g)   + $4H_2O$ (l)

10 cm^3 of propane gas is mixed with 75 cm^3 of oxygen and the mixture exploded. The remaining gases are allowed to cool to room temperature. Calculate the volume and composition of the gas mixture.

6. A mixture of 80 cm^3 of CO and 150 cm^3 of O_2 is exploded.
    (a) Write a balanced equation for the reaction.
    (b) After cooling, the remaining gases are shaken with dilute sodium hydroxide solution.
        i)   Which gas is absorbed by the sodium hydroxide solution?
        ii) What is the reduction in volume of the residual gases after shaking with the solution?
        iii) What volume of gas remains?

7. A gas mixture contains equal volumes of methane and hydrogen.

    Calculate the minimum volume of oxygen required for the complete combustion of 200 cm^3 of this mixture.

8. Xenon gas reacts with fluorine gas to form xenon hexafluoride, XeF_6, a white solid at room temperature and atmospheric pressure.
    (a) Write a balanced equation, with state symbols, for this reaction.
    (b) 50 cm^3 of xenon and 400 cm^3 of fluorine are mixed together. After the reaction, the remaining gases are allowed to cool to room temperature and atmospheric pressure.
        i) Which of the reactant gases is in excess?
        ii) Calculate the remaining volume of this gas.

9. A mixture of 60 cm^3 of H_2 and 40 cm^3 of CO is passed over excess hot copper(II) oxide until no further reaction occurred. The product gases are H_2O and CO_2. The gases are allowed to cool to room temperature.

    Calculate the volume of the resulting gas.

10. 100 cm^3 of butane is mixed with 900 cm^3 of oxygen and the mixture exploded. The remaining gases are allowed to cool to room temperature. Calculate the volume and composition of the gas mixture.

11. 100 cm^3 of an unknown hydrocarbon gas, C_xH_y, when completely burned, required 450 cm^3 of oxygen and produced 300 cm^3 of carbon dioxide. Calculate values for each of **X** and **Y**.

12. Gas syringes are graduated to allow the volume of gases to be measured. A heated box kept a syringe at a temperature greater than 100 $^{\circ}$C. The syringe contained 150 cm^3 of hydrogen and 50 cm^3 of carbon monoxide mixed with 200 cm^3 of oxygen. When ignited the gases reacted as shown.

$$CO\ (g)\ +\ 3H_2\ (g)\ +\ 2O_2\ (g)\ \rightarrow\ CO_2\ (g)\ +\ 3H_2O\ (g)$$

(a) Name the reactant gas which was in excess and give the remaining volume of this gas.
(b) What was the volume and composition of the products of the reaction?
(c) What would have been the reading on the gas syringe if, at the end of the reaction, the gases had been allowed to cool to room temperature?

13. A syringe was used to study the reactions of hydrocarbons with oxygen at a constant temperature of 120 $^{\circ}$C.
In one experiment, 20 cm^3 of a hydrocarbon gas containing six carbon atoms per molecule was ignited in excess oxygen gas. Carbon dioxide and water were produced.
(a) Calculate the volume of carbon dioxide produced.
(b) 100 cm^3 of water vapour was produced.
What is the molecular formula for the hydrocarbon?

Dynamic equilibrium

1. (a) What is meant by a chemical reaction that is 'at equilibrium'?
    (b) Suggest why the word 'dynamic' is used in association with a chemical reaction at equilibrium.

2. State what is meant by a chemical reaction in which the equilibrium
    (a) lies to the left,
    (b) lies to the right.

3. The diagram below shows how the concentration of reactants and products change as a reaction reaches equilibrium.

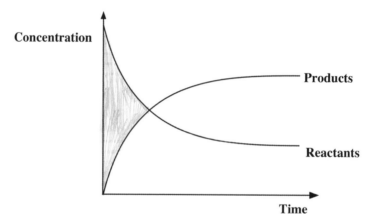

    (a) Copy the diagram and use a vertical line to mark the time at which equilibrium is established.
    (b) i) Does the equilibrium lie to the left or to the right?
        ii) Explain your answer.

4. A student wrote the following **incorrect** statement.

    When a reaction is at equilibrium the concentration of reactants and products are equal.

    Explain the mistake in the student's reasoning.

5. $N_2(g)$ + $2O_2(g)$ $\rightleftharpoons$ $2NO_2(g)$ $\Delta H = +180$ kJ mol^{-1}

Predict how the equilibrium concentration of nitrogen dioxide would be affected by
Chemical
(a) increasing the temperature,
(b) decreasing the pressure,
(c) decreasing the concentration of oxygen.

6. Ozone, O_3, may be produced in the laboratory by electrical discharge.

$3O_2(g)$ $\rightleftharpoons$ $2O_3(g)$ $\Delta H = +285.5$ kJ mol^{-1}

Predict how the equilibrium would be affected by
(a) an increase in pressure,
(b) an increase in temperature.

7. $ICl_3(l)$ + $Cl_2(g)$ $\rightleftharpoons$ $ICl_5(s)$ ΔH is -ve
    (brown liquid)   (yellow solid)

Predict what would be **seen** to happen to a mixture at equilibrium if
(a) more chlorine was added,
(b) the temperature was increased,
(c) the pressure was decreased.

8. $N_2O_4(g)$ $\rightleftharpoons$ $2NO_2(g)$ ΔH is +ve
    (pale yellow)   (dark brown)

Explain what would be **seen** to happen if the equilibrium mixture was
(a) placed in a freezing mixture,
(b) compressed.

9. A mixture of carbon monoxide and hydrogen can be used to produce methane.

$CO(g)$ + $3H_2(g)$ $\rightleftharpoons$ $CH_4(g)$ + $H_2O(g)$ ΔH is -206 kJ mol^{-1}

Give **TWO** reasons why the yield of methane can be increased by cooling the reaction mixture from 400 °C to 80 °C.

10. Synthesis gas, a mixture of hydrogen and carbon monoxide, is prepared as shown.

$$CH_4 (g) \quad + \quad H_2O (g) \rightleftharpoons \quad 3H_2 (g) \quad + \quad CO (g)$$

(a) An increase in temperature increases the yield of synthesis gas. What information does this give about the enthalpy change for the forward reaction?
(b) Explain how a change in pressure will affect the composition of the equilibrium mixture.

11. Ethanol is produced industrially at 70 atmospheres pressure and 300 °C.

$$C_2H_4 (g) \quad + \quad H_2O (g) \rightleftharpoons \quad C_2H_5OH (g) \quad AH = -46 \text{ kJ mol}^{-1}$$

(a) Explain why the yield of ethanol is increased by
    i) decreasing the temperature,
    ii) increasing the pressure.
(b) Suggest why the industrial process is **not** carried out
    i) at temperatures much below 300 °C,
    ii) at pressures much above 70 atmospheres.

12. Ammonia gas dissolves in water to form an alkaline solution.

$$NH_3 (g) \quad + \quad H_2O (l) \rightleftharpoons NH_4^+ (aq) + OH^- (aq) \quad AH = -30.6 \text{ kJ mol}^{-1}$$

Predict how each of the following changes would affect the equilibrium position.
(a) increasing the temperature
(b) increasing the pressure
(c) adding an alkali
(d) adding a dilute acid

13. Reaction 1: H_2 (g) + I_2 (g) $\rightleftharpoons$ 2HI (g)

    Reaction 2: 2CO (g) + O_2 (g) $\rightleftharpoons$ $2CO_2$ (g)

    Reaction 3: CH_3OH (g) $\rightleftharpoons$ CO (g) + $2H_2$ (g)

    Reaction 4: C(s) + CO_2 (g) $\rightleftharpoons$ 2CO (g)

   (a) For each of the above reactions decide whether an increase in pressure will
     i)   shift the position of equilibrium to the left,
     ii) have no effect on the equilibrium position,
     iii) shift the position of equilibrium to the right.
   (b) In reaction 1, the forward reaction is exothermic.
     What effect, if any, will an increase in temperature have on the equilibrium position?

14. In Britain, the main source of magnesium is sea water. One stage in the production of magnesium is shown in the diagram.

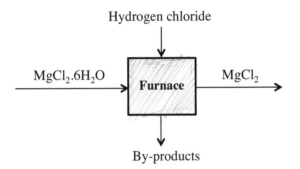

Hydrogen chloride

$MgCl_2.6H_2O$ → **Furnace** → $MgCl_2$

By-products

In the furnace, the water of crystallisation in the $MgCl_2.6H_2O$ is removed by heating. However this can cause the formation of magnesium oxide.

$MgCl_2.6H_2O$ $\rightleftharpoons$ MgO + 2HCl + $5H_2O$

   (a) Which chemical is used to prevent this?
   (b) Explain how this chemical prevents the formation of magnesium oxide.

15. The major reactions in two industrial processes are shown.

Process	Equation	Temp. / °C	Press. / atm	ΔH / kJmol⁻¹
A	$N_2(g) + 3H_2(g) \rightleftharpoons 2NH_3(g)$	400	200	-92
B	$4NH_3(g) + 7O_2(g) \rightleftharpoons$ $4NO_2(g) + 6H_2O(g)$	400	4	-909

(a) Explain whether the temperatures used in the **two** reactions are consistent with the enthalpy changes involved.
(b) Justify the use of high pressure in Process **A** but **not** Process **B**.

16. Sulphuric acid is produced in industry by the Contact Process. The reaction that takes place using a catalyst is:

$$2SO_2(g) + O_2(g) \rightleftharpoons 2SO_3(g)$$

(a) State the effect of a catalyst on
  i)   the rate of the forward reaction,
  ii) the rate of the backward reaction,
  iii) the rate of formation of product,
  iv) the composition of the equilibrium mixture.
(b) Suggest why the reaction is carried out at atmospheric pressure rather than a significantly higher pressure.
(c) The graph shows how the percentage yield changes with temperature.

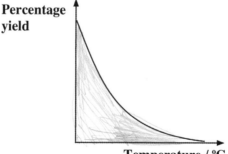

i) Is the reaction exothermic or endothermic?
ii) Explain your answer.

17. The industrial preparation of methanol involves the combination of carbon monoxide and hydrogen.

$$CO\,(g)\ +\ 2H_2\,(g)\ \rightleftharpoons\ CH_3OH\,(g)$$

The curves show the percentages of methanol in the equilibrium mixture under different conditions.

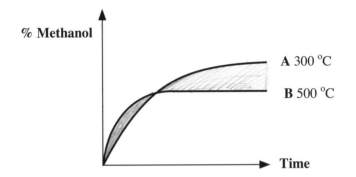

(a) In industry, the reaction is usually carried out at 300 atmospheres pressure. Explain the use of high pressure.

(b) i)   Is the reaction that produces methanol exothermic or endothermic?

    ii)   Explain your answer.

18. When bromine is added to water, a brown solution is formed. The following equilibrium is set up.

$$Br_2\,(aq)\ +\ H_2O\,(l)\ \rightleftharpoons\ BrO^-\,(aq)\ +\ Br^-\,(aq)\ +\ 2H^+\,(aq)$$

(brown
solution)

Explain what would happen to the colour of bromine solution on the addition of

(a) hydrochloric acid,

(b) silver nitrate solution.

(You may wish to refer to the solubility table in the Data Booklet.)

19. When chlorine is dissolved in water the following equilibrium is set up.

$$Cl_2 (aq) \quad + \quad H_2O (l) \quad \rightleftharpoons \quad 2H^+ (aq) \quad + \quad ClO^- (aq) \quad + \quad Cl^- (aq)$$

The hypochlorite ion, ClO^-, is responsible for the bleaching action of the solution.

What effect on the bleaching efficiency of a solution of chlorine in water would each of the following have?

(a) adding dilute nitric acid
(b) adding sodium chloride crystals
(c) adding sodium sulphate crystals
(d) adding potassium hydroxide solution

(You may wish to refer to the solubility table in the Data Booklet.)

20. Potassium iodide solution does not mix with chloroform when both are added to a test tube.
Iodine is then added and dissolves in both potassium iodide solution and chloroform. The test tube is shaken until equilibrium is reached and so no further change is visible.

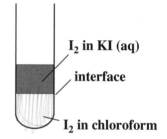

I_2 in KI (aq)

interface

I_2 in chloroform

(a) Explain what is happening at the interface after equilibrium is reached.
(b) What will be seen immediately after more chloroform is added?

21. Calcium sulphate is only sparingly soluble in water. It forms an equilibrium mixture.

$$CaSO_4 (s) \quad \rightleftharpoons \quad Ca^{2+} (aq) \quad + \quad SO_4^{2-} (aq)$$

Predict how the equilibrium mixture would be affected by adding
(a) dilute nitric acid,
(b) dilute sulphuric acid,
(c) barium chloride solution.

(You may wish to refer to the solubility table in the Data Booklet.)

Percentage yield

1. For a chemical reaction, state what is meant by
   (a) the actual yield,
   (b) the theoretical yield.

2. Write the equation that is used to calculate the percentage yield for a chemical reaction.

3. Calculate the percentage yield in each of the following reactions.

   (a) $C_3H_7OH \quad \longrightarrow \quad C_2H_5CHO$

   In a preparation, 3.2 g of propanal is obtained from 3.9 g of propan-1-ol.

   (b) $C_3H_6 \quad + \quad Br_2 \quad \longrightarrow \quad C_3H_6Br_2$

   In a preparation, 20.4 g of 1,2-dibromopropane is obtained from 5.2 g of propene.

   (c) $CH_3OH \quad + \quad C_2H_5COOH \quad \rightleftharpoons \quad C_2H_5COOCH_3 \quad + \quad H_2O$

   In a preparation, 40.4 g of methyl propanoate is obtained from 18.3 g of methanol.

   (d) $N_2\,(g) \quad + \quad 3H_2\,(g) \quad \rightleftharpoons \quad 2NH_3\,(g)$

   Under test conditions, 2 kg of hydrogen reacts with excess nitrogen to produce 10 kg of ammonia.

   (e) $C_2H_4\,(g) \quad + \quad H_2O\,(g) \quad \rightleftharpoons \quad C_2H_5OH\,(g)$

   Under test conditions, 580 kg of ethanol is produced from 400 kg of ethene.

   (f) $SO_2\,(g) \quad + \quad O_2\,(g) \quad \rightleftharpoons \quad SO_3\,(g)$

   Under test conditions, 1 tonne of sulphur dioxide reacts with excess oxygen to produce 0.83 tonnes of sulphur trioxide.

4. Calculate the mass of the named product that would be formed in each of the following reactions.

(a) C_2H_5OH + CH_3COOH $\rightleftharpoons$ $CH_3COOC_2H_5$ + H_2O
ethylethanoate

The percentage yield from 4.6 g of ethanol is 81%.

(b) CH_3CHO $\rightleftharpoons$ CH_3COOH
ethanoic acid

The percentage yield from 2.7 g of ethanal is 63%.

(c) C_2H_4 (g) + H_2O (g) $\rightleftharpoons$ C_2H_5OH (g)
ethanol

The percentage yield from 1000 kg of ethene is 80%.

(d) CH_3COOCH_3 $\rightleftharpoons$ $HCOOH$ + CH_3OH
methanoic acid

The percentage yield from 2.1 g of methylethanoate is 73 %.

(e) SO_2 (g) + O_2 (g) $\rightleftharpoons$ SO_3 (g)
sulphur trioxide

The percentage yield from 250 kg of sulphur dioxide is 71 %.

(f) $4NH_3$ (g) + O_2 (g) $\rightleftharpoons$ $4NO_2$ (g) + $6H_2O$ (g)
**nitrogen
dioxide**

The percentage yield from 10 tonnes of ammonia is 67 %.

Atom economy

1. (a) What is meant by the atom economy for a chemical reaction?
   (b) Write the equation that is used to calculate the atom economy.

2. Why can a reaction with a high atom economy be considered to be 'greener' than a reaction with a low atom economy?

3. Calculate the atom economy for each of the following reactions.

   (a) Making ethanol from ethene

   $$C_2H_4 \quad + \quad H_2O \quad \rightarrow \quad C_2H_5OH$$

   (b) Making iron from iron(III) oxide

   $$Fe_2O_3 \quad + \quad 3CO \quad \rightarrow \quad 2Fe \quad + \quad CO_2$$

   (c) Making calcium oxide from calcium carbonate

   $$CaCO_3 \quad \rightarrow \quad CaO \quad + \quad CO_2$$

   (d) The fermentation of glucose to produce ethanol

   $$C_6H_{12}O_6 \quad \rightarrow \quad 2C_2H_5OH \quad + \quad 2CO_2$$

   (e) Making hydrazine, N_2H_4

   $$2NH_3 \quad + \quad NaOCl \quad \rightarrow \quad N_2H_4 \quad + \quad NaCl \quad + \quad H_2O$$

4. Ammonia can be made by the Haber process.

   $$N_2 \quad + \quad 3H_2 \quad \rightarrow \quad 2NH_3$$

   Ammonia can also be made by the reaction of ammonium chloride with calcium oxide.

   $$CaO \quad + \quad 2NH_4Cl \quad \rightarrow \quad CaCl_2 \quad + \quad H_2O \quad + \quad 2NH_3$$

   (a) Calculate the atom economy for each method of making ammonia.
   (b) i) Which method can be considered to be greener?
       ii) Explain your answer.

Enthalpy of combustion

1. What is meant by the enthalpy of combustion?

2. Write the balanced equation for the enthalpy of combustion of
   (a) methanol,
   (b) ethanol.

3. Give **TWO** reasons for a data book value for the enthalpy of combustion of an alcohol being different from the value calculated in the laboratory using a spirit burner.

4. Dimethyl ether has the same molecular formula as ethanol.

   $$CH_3 - O - CH_3 \qquad\qquad CH_3 - CH_2 - OH$$
   dimethyl ether **ethanol**

   Why then does it have a different enthalpy of combustion?

5. The enthalpies of combustion of methanol, ethanol and propan-1-ol are -726, -1367 and -2021 kJmol^{-1} respectively.
   (a) Why is there a regular increase in enthalpies of combustion from methanol to ethanol to propan-1-ol?
   (b) Estimate the enthalpy of combustion of butan-1-ol.

   In Questions 6 to 11, assume no heat loss to the surroundings.

6. Calculate the enthalpy of combustion for each of the carbon compounds using the information given.
   (a) When 1 g of ethane burned, 50 kJ of energy was given out.
   (b) When 10 g of butane burned, 469 kJ of energy was given out.

7. Calculate the enthalpy of combustion for each of the carbon compounds using the information given.
   (a) When 1.1 g of methanol burned, the energy produced raised the temperature of 100 cm^3 of water by 57°C.
   (b) When 5.9 g of ethanol burned, the energy produced raised the temperature of 1 litre of water from 14.7 °C to 53.8 °C.

8. When 1 g of sulphur was completely burned in air, the heat produced warmed 110 g of water from 18 °C to 38 °C.

   Calculate the enthalpy of combustion of sulphur.

   In Questions 9 to 11, use the enthalpies of combustion given in the Data Booklet.

9. Calculate the quantity of energy given out by the complete combustion of each the carbon compounds.
   (a) 1 g of ethene
   (b) 8 g of hydrogen

10. (a) Calculate the mass of methane that, on complete combustion, would produce 21.3 kJ.
    (b) Calculate the mass of propane that, on complete combustion, would produce 5000 kJ.

11. (a) Calculate the mass of methanol that, on complete combustion, would produce the energy required to raise the temperature of 2 litres of water by 63 °C.
    (b) Calculate the mass of ethanol that, on complete combustion, would produce the energy required to raise the temperature of 500 cm^3 of water from 17.2 °C to 51.7 °C.

Hess's Law

1. The following three reactions can be used to confirm Hess's law.

		KOH (s)	➜	KOH (aq)			$\Delta H = $ **a**
KOH (s)	+	HCl (aq)	➜	KCl (aq)	+	H_2O (l)	$\Delta H = $ **b**
KOH (aq)	+	HCl (aq)	➜	KCl (aq)	+	H_2O (l)	$\Delta H = $ **c**

    (a) Use Hess's law to write an equation to show the relationship between **a**, **b**, and **c**.
    (b) Write in words a statement of Hess's law.

2. Use the information below to calculate the enthalpy of solution of sodium hydroxide:

    $$NaOH \text{ (s)} \ ➜ \ NaOH\text{(aq)}$$

    $$NaOH \text{ (s)} + HCl \text{ (aq)} ➜ NaCl\text{(aq)} + H_2O \text{ (l)} \quad \Delta H = \text{-105 kJ mol}^{-1}$$

    $$NaOH \text{ (aq)} + HCl \text{ (aq)} ➜ NaCl\text{(aq)} + H_2O \text{ (l)} \quad \Delta H = \text{-65.8 kJ mol}^{-1}$$

3.

Enthalpy change	ΔH / kJ mol^{-1}
$RbCl$ (s) ➜ Rb^+ (aq) + Cl^- (aq)	+17
Rb^+ (g) ➜ Rb^+ (aq)	-301
Cl^- (g) ➜ Cl^- (aq)	-364

Calculate the enthalpy of lattice breaking for rubidium chloride:

$$RbCl \text{ (s)} \qquad ➜ \qquad Rb^+ \text{ (g)} \quad + \quad Cl^- \text{ (g)}$$

4. Use the information below to calculate the enthalpy of combustion of carbon monoxide.

2C (g)	+	O_2 (g)	➜	2CO (g)	$\Delta H = $	-216 kJ
C (g)	+	O_2 (g)	➜	CO_2 (g)	$\Delta H = $	-394 kJ

5. Use the information below to calculate the enthalpy change for the reaction:

$$3C\ (g) \quad + \quad 4H_2\ (g) \quad \rightarrow \quad C_3H_8\ (g)$$

Enthalpy change	ΔH / kJ mol^{-1}
$C\ (s) \quad \rightarrow \quad C\ (g)$	+715
$3C\ (s) \quad + \quad 4H_2\ (g) \quad \rightarrow \quad C_3H_8\ (g)$	-104

6. Use the information below to calculate the enthalpy change for the reaction:

$$C_2H_4\ (g) \quad + \quad H_2\ (g) \quad \rightarrow \quad C_2H_6\ (g)$$

Enthalpy change	ΔH / kJ mol^{-1}
$H_2\ (g) \quad + \quad \frac{1}{2}O_2\ (g) \quad \rightarrow \quad H_2O\ (l)$	-286
$C_2H_4\ (g) \quad + \quad 3O_2\ (g) \quad \rightarrow \quad 2CO_2\ (g) \quad + \quad 2H_2O\ (l)$	-1411
$C_2H_6\ (g) \quad + \quad 3\frac{1}{2}O_2\ (g) \quad \rightarrow \quad 2CO_2\ (g) \quad + \quad 3H_2O\ (l)$	-1561

7. Use the information below to calculate the enthalpy change for the reaction:

$$3C\ (s) \quad + \quad H_2\ (g) \quad + \quad Cl_2\ (g) \quad \rightarrow \quad CH_2Cl_2\ (g)$$

Enthalpy change	ΔH / kJ mol^{-1}
$CH_2Cl_2\ (g) \quad + \quad O_2\ (g) \quad \rightarrow \quad CO_2\ (g) \quad + \quad 2HCl\ (g)$	-446
$C\ (s) \quad + \quad O_2\ (g) \quad \rightarrow \quad CO_2\ (g)$	-394
$H_2\ (g) \quad + \quad Cl_2\ (g) \quad \rightarrow \quad 2HCl\ (g)$	-104

8. The enthalpy of formation of ethanol is the enthalpy change for the reaction:

$$2C (s) + 3H_2 (g) + \tfrac{1}{2}O_2 (g) \rightarrow C_2H_5OH (l)$$

Use the enthalpies of combustion of carbon, hydrogen and ethanol given in the Data Booklet to calculate the enthalpy of formation of ethanol.

9. The enthalpy of formation of propan-1-ol is the enthalpy change for the reaction:

$$3C (s) + 4H_2 (g) + \tfrac{1}{2}O_2 (g) \rightarrow C_3H_7OH (l)$$
propan-1-ol

Calculate the enthalpy of formation of propan-1-ol using the enthalpies of combustion given in the Data Booklet.

10. The enthalpy of formation of butane is the enthalpy change for the reaction:

$$4C (s) + 5H_2 (g) \rightarrow C_4H_{10} (g) \qquad \Delta H = -128 \text{ kJ mol}^{-1}$$

Calculate the enthalpy of combustion of butane using the enthalpy of formation of butane and the enthalpies of combustion of carbon and hydrogen given in the Data Booklet.

11. The enthalpy of formation of cyclohexane (C_6H_{12}) is the enthalpy change for the reaction:

$$6C (s) + 3H_2 (g) \rightarrow C_6H_{12} (l)$$

Use the enthalpies of combustion given in the Data Booklet to calculate the enthalpy of formation of cyclohexane.

(Take the enthalpy of combustion of cyclohexane to be -3920 kJ mol^{-1}.)

12. Use the enthalpies of combustion given in the Data Booklet to calculate the enthalpy change for the reaction:

$$2C \text{ (s)} \quad + \quad 3H_2 \text{ (g)} \quad \rightarrow \quad C_2H_6 \text{ (g)}$$

13. CH_3NHNH_2 (l) + $^5/_2O_2$ (g) → CO_2 (g) + $3H_2O$ (l) + N_2 (g)

    methylhydrazine $\Delta H = -1305kJ$

    Using this information, together with the enthalpies of combustion in the Data Booklet, calculate the enthalpy change for the reaction:

    $$C\text{(s)} \quad + \quad 3H_2 \text{ (g)} \quad + \quad N_2 \text{ (g)} \quad \rightarrow \quad CH_3NHNH_2 \text{ (l)}$$

14. Use the enthalpy changes given in the table to calculate the enthalpy of combustion of the gas diborane, B_2H_6.

Enthalpy change	ΔH / kJ mol^{-1}
$2B \text{ (s)} \quad + \quad 3H_2 \text{ (g)} \quad \rightarrow \quad B_2H_6 \text{ (g)}$	+32
$H_2 \text{ (g)} \quad + \quad ^1/_2O_2 \text{ (g)} \quad \rightarrow \quad H_2O \text{ (l)}$	-286
$2B \text{ (s)} \quad + \quad ^3/_2O_2 \text{ (g)} \quad \rightarrow \quad B_2O_3 \text{ (s)}$	-1225

15. The equation for the enthalpy of formation of ethanoic acid is:

    $$2C \text{ (s)} \quad + \quad 2H_2 \text{ (g)} \quad + \quad O_2 \text{ (g)} \quad \rightarrow \quad CH_3COOH \text{ (l)}$$

    Calculate the enthalpy change for the above reaction using enthalpy changes in the Data Booklet and the following information.

    $$CH_3COOH \text{ (l)} \quad + \quad 2O_2 \text{ (g)} \rightarrow 2CO_2 \text{ (g)} + H_2O \text{ (l)} \quad \Delta H = -876 \text{ kJ mol}^{-1}$$

Bond enthalpy

1. Copy and complete the following sentences.
   (a) Bond breaking is an .... reaction.
   (b) Bond making is an .... reaction.

2. (a) What is meant by the bond enthalpy?
   (b) What is meant by the **mean** bond enthalpy?
   (c) Why is the C – H bond listed in the Data Booklet as a mean bond enthalpy and yet the Cl – Cl bond is listed as a bond enthalpy?

3. Use the bond enthalpies (or mean bond enthalpies) given in the Data Booklet to calculate the enthalpy change for each of the following gaseous reactions.

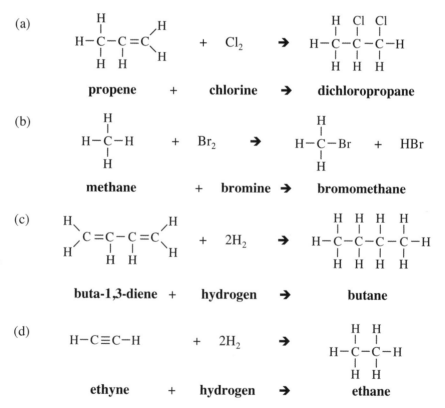

(a)

propene   +   chlorine   ➔   dichloropropane

(b)

methane   +   bromine ➔ bromomethane

(c)

buta-1,3-diene + hydrogen   ➔   butane

(d)

ethyne   +   hydrogen   ➔   ethane

(e) H_2 (g)   + F_2 (g)   → $2HF$ (g)

(f) C_3H_6 (g)   + H_2 (g)   → C_3H_8 (g)

(g) CH_4 (g)   + $2O_2$ (g)   → CO_2 (g)   + $2H_2O$ (g)

(h) C_2H_4 (g)   + H_2O (g)   → C_2H_5OH (g)

(i) ethene   +   hydrogen   →   ethane

(j) nitrogen   +   hydrogen   →   ammonia

(k) hydrogen   +   chlorine   →   hydrogen chloride

(l) but-2-ene   +   hydrogen bromide   →   2-bromobutane

Oxidation and reduction (revision)

1. State what is meant by
   (a) oxidation,
   (b) reduction.

2. Copy and complete the following sentences.
   (a) A metal element reacting to form a compound is an example of ....
   (b) A compound reacting to form a metal element is an example of ....

3. Use the Data Booklet to write an ion-electron equation for each of the following reactions.
   (a) the oxidation of magnesium atoms
   (b) the oxidation of iron(II) ions
   (c) the oxidation of iodide ions
   (d) the reduction of aluminium ions
   (e) the reduction of chlorine molecules
   (f) the reduction of dichromate ions in acid solution

Redox reactions

1. What is meant by a redox reaction?

2. For each of the following, combine the two ion-electron equations to write the overall redox equation.

(a) $Al (s) \rightarrow Al^{3+} (aq) + 3e^-$
$2H^+ (aq) + 2e^- \rightarrow H_2 (g)$

(b) $Ce^{4+} (aq) + e^- \rightarrow Ce^{3+} (aq)$
$2Br^- (aq) \rightarrow Br_2 (g) + 2e^-$

(c) $Cu (s) \rightarrow Cu^{2+} (aq) + 2e^-$
$Ag^+ (aq) + e^- \rightarrow Ag (s)$

(d) $MnO_4^- (aq) + 8H^+ (aq) + 5e^- \rightarrow Mn^{2+} (aq) + 3H_2O (l)$
$Fe^{2+} (aq) \rightarrow Fe^{3+} (aq) + e^-$

(e) $Cr_2O_7^{2-} (aq) + 14H^+ (aq) + 6e^- \rightarrow 2Cr^{3+} (aq) + 7H_2O (l)$
$Sn^{2+} (aq) \rightarrow Sn^{4+} (aq) + 2e^-$

3. For each of the following redox equations, write an ion-electron equation for the oxidation and reduction steps.

(a) $Cl_2 (g) + 2Fe^{2+} (aq) \rightarrow 2Cl^- (aq) + 2Fe^{3+} (aq)$

(b) $Zn (s) + Cu^{2+} (aq) \rightarrow Zn^{2+} (aq) + Cu (s)$

(c) $Mg (s) + 2H^+ (aq) \rightarrow Mg^{2+} (aq) + H_2 (g)$

(d) $Cl_2 (g) + 2KBr (aq) \rightarrow Br_2 (aq) + 2KCl (aq)$

(e) $Cu (s) + 2AgNO_3 (aq) \rightarrow Cu(NO_3)_2 (aq) + 2Ag (s)$

(f) $Fe (s) + 2HCl (aq) \rightarrow FeCl_2 (aq) + H_2 (g)$

(g) $Na_2SO_3 (aq) + H_2O (l) + I_2 (aq)$
$\rightarrow Na_2SO_4 (aq) + 2H^+ (aq) + 2I^- (aq)$

(h) $6Fe^{2+} (aq) + Cr_2O_7^{2-} (aq) + 14H^+ (aq)$
$\rightarrow 6Fe^{3+} (aq) + 2Cr^{3+} (aq) + 7H_2O (l)$

4. (a) Some carbon monoxide detectors contain crystals of hydrated palladium(II) chloride. These form palladium in a redox reaction if exposed to carbon monoxide.

$$CO\,(g) \quad + \quad PdCl_2.2H_2O\,(s)$$
$$\rightarrow \quad CO_2\,(g) \; + \; Pd\,(s) \; + \; 2HCl\,(g) \; + \; 7H_2O\,(l)$$

Write the ion-electron equation for the reduction step in this reaction.

(b) Another type of detector uses an electrochemical method to detect carbon monoxide.

At the positive electrode:

$$CO\,(g) \quad + \quad H_2O\,(l) \quad \rightarrow \quad CO_2\,(g) \; + \; 2H^+\,(aq) \; + \; 2e^-$$

At the negative electrode:

$$O_2\,(g) \quad + \quad 4H^+\,(aq) \quad + \quad 4e^- \rightarrow \quad 2H_2O\,(l)$$

Combine the two ion-electron equations to give the overall redox equation.

5. For each of the following reactions, write an ion-electron equation for the oxidation and reduction steps.

Combine the oxidation and reduction steps to form the overall redox reaction.

(a) Zinc reduces aqueous silver ions.

(b) Fluorine solution oxidises iodide ions.

(c) Magnesium reduces hydrogen ions.

(d) Sulphite ions reduce bromine solution.

(e) Permanganate ions oxidise iron(II) ions in acid solution.

(f) Dichromate ions oxidise tin(II) ions in acid solution.

(g) Sodium sulphite reduces bromine solution.

(h) Potassium iodide reduces chlorine solution.

(i) Potassium permanganate oxidises hydrochloric acid to chlorine.

(j) In acid solution, potassium dichromate oxidises sodium sulphite solution.

(k) In acid solution, potassium permanganate oxidises sodium bromide.

Chemistry in Society

Writing ion-electron equations

1. Write a balanced ion-electron equation for each of the following reactions.

   (a) SO_3^{2-} (aq) $\rightarrow$ SO_4^{2-} (aq)

   (b) MnO_4^- (aq) $\rightarrow$ Mn^{2+} (aq)

   (c) IO_3^- (aq) $\rightarrow$ I_2 (aq)

   (d) PbO_2 (s) $\rightarrow$ Pb^{2+} (aq)

   (e) XeO_3 (aq) $\rightarrow$ Xe (g)

   (f) ClO^- (aq) $\rightarrow$ Cl^- (aq)

   (g) $Cr_2O_7^{2-}$ (aq) $\rightarrow$ $2Cr^{3+}$ (aq)

2. Acrylonitrile (CH_2CHCN) can be reduced in neutral aqueous solution. Hydroxide ions are produced in the reaction.

   Copy the equation below and complete to form the balanced ion-electron equation for the reaction.

   CH_2CHCN $\rightarrow$ $(CH_2CH_2CN)_2$ + OH^- (aq)

Oxidising and reducing agents

1. State what is meant by
   (a) an oxidising agent,
   (b) a reducing agent.

2. (a) Name **TWO** oxidising agents that have everyday uses.
   (b) Give a use for each.

3. For each of the following reactions, identify the oxidising and reducing agent.

   (a) Cl_2 (g) + 2Br⁻ (aq) ➜ 2Cl⁻ (aq) + Br_2 (aq)

   (b) Mg (s) + Cu^{2+} (aq) ➜ Mg^{2+} (aq) + Cu (s)

   (c) Fe (s) + $2H^+$ (aq) ➜ Fe^{2+} (aq) + H_2 (g)

   (d) Br_2 (g) + 2KI (aq) ➜ I_2 (aq) + 2KBr (aq)

   (e) Zn (s) + H_2SO_4 (aq) ➜ $ZnSO_4$ (aq) + H_2 (g)

   (f) Na_2SO_3 (aq) + H_2O (l) + I_2 (aq)
      ➜ Na_2SO_4 (aq) + $2H^+$ (aq) + 2I⁻ (aq)

   (g) $6Fe^{2+}$ (aq) + $Cr_2O_7^{2-}$ (aq) + $14H^+$ (aq)
      ➜ $6Fe^{3+}$ (aq) + $2Cr^{3+}$ (aq) + $7H_2O$ (l)

Neutralisation (revision)

1. The equation for the reaction between sodium hydroxide solution and dilute hydrochloric acid is:

$$NaOH\,(aq) \quad + \quad HCl\,(aq) \quad \rightarrow \quad NaCl\,(aq) \quad + \quad H_2O\,(l)$$

In one titration, 25 cm^3 of sodium hydroxide solution (concentration 0.1 mol l^{-1}) was neutralised by 37.4 cm^3 of a dilute acid.

(a) Calculate the number of moles of sodium hydroxide used in the titration.

(b) Calculate the concentration of the dilute hydrochloric acid.

2. (a) $$HCl\,(aq) \quad + \quad NaOH\,(aq) \quad \rightarrow \quad NaCl\,(aq) \quad + \quad H_2O\,(l)$$

What volume of hydrochloric acid (concentration 0.1 mol l^{-1}) is required to neutralise 50 cm^3 of sodium hydroxide solution (concentration 0.2 mol l^{-1})?

(b) $$H_2SO_4\,(aq) \quad + \quad 2KOH\,(aq) \quad \rightarrow \quad K_2SO_4\,(aq) \quad + \quad 2H_2O\,(l)$$

What is the concentration of sulphuric acid if 50 cm^3 neutralises 25 cm^3 of potassium hydroxide solution (concentration 1 mol l^{-1})?

3. (a) What is the concentration of hydrochloric acid if 12.6 cm^3 neutralises 20 cm^3 of potassium hydroxide solution (concentration 0.1 mol l^{-1})?

(b) What volume of nitric acid (concentration 2 mol l^{-1}) is required to neutralise 20 cm^3 of sodium hydroxide solution (concentration 0.5 mol l^{-1})?

(c) What is the concentration of sulphuric acid if 17.3 cm^3 neutralises 25 cm^3 of sodium hydroxide solution (concentration 0.5 mol l^{-1})?

4. Vinegar is a dilute solution of ethanoic acid in water. A student carried out a titration, using 0.1 mol l^{-1} sodium hydroxide solution, to find out the concentration of ethanoic acid in some vinegar.
    The average volume of sodium hydroxide solution that was used to neutralise 25 cm^3 of vinegar was 20 cm^3.
    (a) Calculate the number of moles of sodium hydroxide in this average volume.
    (b) **One** mole of ethanoic acid reacts with **one** mole of sodium hydroxide. Calculate the concentration of ethanoic acid, in mol l^{-1}, in the vinegar.

5. A student added 0.5 mol l^{-1} sulphuric acid from a burette to 20 cm^3 of 0.5 mol l^{-1} ammonia solution in a conical flask with pH indicator.
    The equation for the reaction is:

    $$2NH_3 \text{ (aq)} \quad + \quad H_2SO_4 \text{ (aq)} \quad \rightarrow \quad (NH_4)_2SO_4 \text{ (aq)}$$

    Calculate the volume of sulphuric acid that was used to neutralise the ammonia solution.

6. The concentration of dissolved calcium ions in a sample of hard water can be found by titration with an acid called EDTA, using a suitable indicator.
    One mole of calcium ions reacts with **one** mole of EDTA.
    In one titration 18.6 cm^3 of 0.12 mol l^{-1} EDTA reacted with 25.0 cm^3 of a water sample.

    Calculate the concentration of calcium ions, in mol l^{-1}, in the sample.

Redox titrations

1. Iron(II) ions react with dichromate ions in acidic solution.

   $6Fe^{2+}$ (aq)   + $Cr_2O_7^{2-}$ (aq)   + $14H^+$ (aq)
   $\rightarrow$ $6Fe^{3+}$ (aq)   + $2Cr^{3+}$ (aq)   + $7H_2O$ (l)

   Calculate the amount of iron(II) ions, in moles, that will react completely with 250 cm^3 of dichromate solution, concentration 0.1 mol l^{-1}.

2. Permanganate ions react with hydrogen peroxide in acidic solution.

   $2MnO_4^-$ (aq)   + $6H^+$ (aq) + $5H_2O_2$ (aq)
   $\rightarrow$ $2Mn^{2+}$ (aq)   + $8H_2O$ (l) + $5O_2$ (g)

   25 cm^3 of hydrogen peroxide solution reacted with 16 cm^3 of permanganate solution, concentration 0.1 mol l^{-1}.

   Calculate the concentration of the hydrogen peroxide solution.

3. Dichromate ions react with ethanol in acidic solution.

   $2Cr_2O_7^{2-}$ (aq) + $16H^+$ (aq)   + $3C_2H_5OH$ (aq)
   $\rightarrow$ $3CH_3COOH$ (aq)   + $4Cr^{3+}$ (aq)   + $11H_2O$ (l)

   It was found that 12.5 cm^3 of 0.1 mol l^{-1} potassium dichromate solution was required to oxidise the ethanol in a 1 cm^3 sample of wine.

   Calculate the mass of ethanol in the 1 cm^3 wine sample.

4. The chlorine levels in swimming pools can be determined by titrating samples against acidified iron(II) sulphate solution.
   The reaction taking place is:

   Cl_2 (aq)   + $2Fe^{2+}$ (aq) $\rightarrow$ $2Cl^-$ (aq)   + $2Fe^{3+}$ (aq)

   A 100 cm^3 sample of water from a swimming pool required 24.9 cm^3 of iron(II) sulphate, concentration 2.82 mol l^{-1}, to reach the end-point.

   Calculate the chlorine concentration, in g l^{-1}, in the swimming pool water.

5. A cigarette lighter flint contained cerium. It was dissolved in 30 cm^3 of dilute sulphuric acid, and heated with a catalyst to produce a solution containing Ce^{4+} (aq) ions.
It was found that 4.85 cm^3 of iron(II) sulphate solution, concentration 0.05 mol l^{-1}, was required to reduce 10 cm^3 of the Ce^{4+} (aq) solution.

Equations:

Fe^{2+} (aq)   ➔ Fe^{3+} (aq)   + e^-

Ce^{4+} (aq)   + e^- ➔ Ce^{3+} (aq)

Calculate the mass of cerium in the flint.

6. Sulphur dioxide is added to wine as a preservative.
The concentration of sulphur dioxide in white wine may be found by titration with a standard solution of iodine.
The equation for the reaction that takes place is:

SO_2 (aq) + I_2 (aq) + $2H_2O$ (l) ➔ $4H^+$ (aq) + SO_4^{2-} (aq) + $2I^-$ (aq)

In one particular titration, it was found that the sulphur dioxide in 100 cm^3 of wine reacted with 11.2 cm^3 of 0.005 mol l^{-1} iodine solution.

Calculate the concentration of sulphur dioxide, in mgl^{-1}, present in the wine.

7. In an experiment to measure the concentration of ozone, O_3, in the air in a Scottish city, 10^5 litres of air were bubbled through a solution of potassium iodide.
Ozone reacts with potassium iodide releasing iodine.

$2KI$ (aq) + O_3 (g) + H_2O (l) ➔ I_2 (aq) + O_2 (g) + $2KOH$ (aq)

The iodine formed was completely oxidised by 22.5 cm^3 of sodium thiosulphate solution, concentration 0.01 mol l^{-1}.

I_2 (aq)   + $2S_2O_3^{2-}$ (aq)   ➔ $2I^-$ (aq)   + $S_4O_6^{2-}$ (aq)

Calculate the volume of ozone in 1 litre of air.

(Take the volume of one mole of ozone to be 24 litres.)

8. The concentration of vitamin C, $C_6H_8O_6$, in a solution can be found by titrating it with a standard solution of iodine.
The equation for the reaction is :

$$C_6H_8O_6 (aq) \ + \ I_2 (aq) \ \rightarrow \ C_6H_6O_6 (aq) \ + \ 2H^+ (aq) \ + \ 2I^- (aq)$$

In one investigation, it was found that an average of 29.5 cm^3 of 0.02 mol l^{-1} iodine solution was required to react completely with 25.0 cm^3 of vitamin C solution.

Use this result to calculate the mass of vitamin C present in the solution.

9. The percentage purity of iron(II) salts can be found by titration with acidified potassium permanganate solution.
The following relationship can be used to calculate the percentage purity of a salt.

$$percentage\ purity \ = \ \frac{mass\ of\ pure\ salt}{mass\ of\ impure\ salt} \ x \ 100$$

A student was given 1.55 g of impure iron(II) sulphate, $FeSO_4.7H_2O$, and used this to prepare 250 cm^3 of solution for the titration. It was found that 9.5 cm^3 of acidified potassium permanganate, concentration 0.01 mol l^{-1}, was required to oxidise 25 cm^3 of the iron(II) sulphate solution.

Equations:
$$Fe^{2+} (aq) \qquad\qquad \rightarrow \qquad Fe^{3+} (aq) \ + \ e^-$$

$$MnO_4^- (aq) \ + \ 8H^+ (aq) + \ 5e^- \ \rightarrow \ Mn^{2+} (aq) \ + \ 4H_2O (l)$$

Calculate the mass of pure iron(II) sulphate and thus find the percentage purity of the iron(II) sulphate salt.

Chromatography

1. A mixture of hexane (C_6H_{12}), dodecane ($C_{12}H_{26}$) and isocane ($C_{20}H_{40}$) was injected into a gas-liquid chromatograph and the chromatogram shown was obtained.

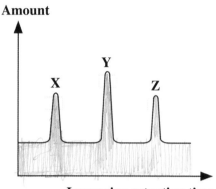

Amount

Increasing retention time

(a) i) Name the alkane that corresponds to each of the peaks **X**, **Y** and **Z**.

ii) Explain your reasoning.

(b) A second sample containing the same volumes of hexane and dodecane but half the volume of isocane was injected into the chromatograph.
Draw a second chromatogram to show the peaks that would be expected.

2. A mixture of one volume of hexane, two volumes of pentan-1-ol and two volumes of butane-1,4-diol was injected into a gas-liquid chromatograph.

$$CH_3-CH_2- CH_2- CH_2-CH_2- CH_3 \qquad \textbf{hexane}$$

$$CH_3- CH_2- CH_2-CH_2- CH_2-OH \qquad \textbf{pentan-1-ol}$$

$$HO- CH_2- CH_2-CH_2- CH_2-OH \qquad \textbf{butane-1,4-diol}$$

(a) i) Draw a chromatogram to show the peaks that would be expected.

ii) Explain your reasoning.

(b) Suggest why pentan-1-ol and butane-1,4-diol were used in the experiment rather than an alcohol and a diol with six carbon atoms per molecule.

3. Chromatogram 1 was obtained using four known compounds **A**, **B**, **C** and **D**. Chromatogram 2 was obtained with an unknown compound.

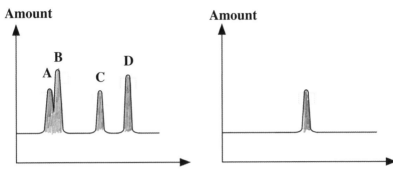

(a) From **A**, **B**, **C** and **D**, identify the unknown compound.
(b) i) What does the chromatogram suggest about the structures of **A** and **B**?
    ii) Why is it difficult to accurately determine the amount of **A** in a sample containing a large amount of **B**.

4. A chemist used paper chromatography to identify amino acids in unknown samples **X**, **Y** and **Z**.
The developed chromatogram is shown below.

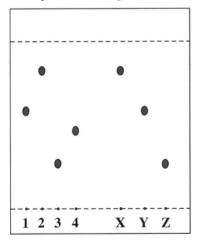

No	Amino acid
1	asparagine
2	phenylalanine
3	glycine
4	tyrosine

(a) Which of the four known amino acids is likely to have the most polar structure?
(b) What can be concluded about each of unknown samples?

Practical skills (i)

1. (a) With volumetric titrations what is the difference between the use of a pipette and a burette?
   (b) Describe how to measure a volume of liquid using a pipette.

2. (a) What is meant by a standard solution?
   (b) Describe how to make up a standard solution.
   (c) Why is distilled (deionised) water used in making up a standard solution?
   (d) Give **TWO** reasons why some solids are unsuitable for making standard solutions.

3. (a) Why is a 1 mg l⁻¹ standard solution **not** prepared by measuring out a mass of 1mg and making up to 1 litre using a volumetric flask?
   (b) Describe the way to make a standard solution of very low concentration, e.g. 1 mg l⁻¹?

4. (a) What is meant by the end-point in a titration?
   (b) Why is the indicator able to detect the end-point in a titration?
   (c) What is meant by a self-indicating reaction?

5. In an investigation to find the concentration of alkali in a water sample, a student carried out three titrations.
   The following results were obtained.

Titration	Volume of acid used / cm³
1	27.7
2	26.8
3	27.0

   One of the titrations can be described as a **<u>rough</u>** titration.
   (a) What is meant by the underlined word?
   (b) How would the student know when to stop adding acid from the burette?
   (c) What volume of acid would be used in the calculation to find the concentration of alkali?

6. The mass of vitamin C in a tablet can be found by titration with iodine.

(a) The following instructions are part of the work-card for this investigation.

> Estimation of vitamin C
>
> 1. Add a vitamin C tablet to about 50 cm^3 of distilled water in a small beaker and stir to dissolve.
>
> 2. Transfer quantitatively to a 250 cm^3 standard flask.

To "transfer quantitatively" means that all of the vitamin C must be transferred to the standard flask.

Describe how this would be carried out in practice.

(b) The picture shows a trainee technician taking a burette reading while carrying out a vitamin C titration.

Identify **FOUR** points of bad practice in his technique.

Practical skills (ii)

1. A hydrocarbon burns to produce carbon dioxide and water. Lime water can be used to detect carbon dioxide in the product of the reaction; the water can be collected for identification by condensing the gas using an ice/salt bath.

    Draw a labelled diagram to show a way to identify the carbon dioxide and a way to collect the water for identification.

2. The reaction of dilute sulphuric acid with calcium carbonate produces carbon dioxide gas. This reaction can be used to investigate the effect of particle size on the rate of reaction.
    (a) Draw a labelled arrangement to show how the carbon dioxide could be produced.
    (b) Extend this arrangement to show a way of collecting the carbon dioxide **in such a way that its volume could be measured**.
    (c) Which variables should be kept constant?

3. The hydrogen produced by the reaction of magnesium with dilute hydrochloric acid can be contaminated with small quantities of hydrogen chloride. Hydrogen chloride reacts with sodium hydroxide.

    Draw a labelled arrangement to show how the hydrogen chloride could be removed from the hydrogen/hydrogen chloride mixture before the hydrogen is collected.

4. The slow reaction between magnesium and water can be used with the equation below to find the molar volume of hydrogen gas.

    $$Mg \ (s) \quad + \quad 2H_2O \ (l) \quad \rightarrow \quad Mg(OH)_2 \ (aq) \quad + \quad H_2 \ (g)$$

    The following items were used in the experiment.

    measuring cylinder, beaker of water, filter funnel, magnesium ribbon

    (a) Draw a diagram to show how the above items would have been arranged at the start of the experiment.
    (b) What **TWO** measurements would be taken?

5. Lithium hydride can be made by bubbling hydrogen through liquid lithium. Draw an arrangement that could be placed between points **A** and **B** to show how the reaction could be carried out.

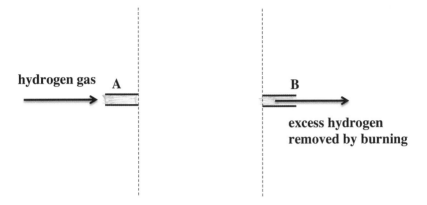

hydrogen gas **A**

B

excess hydrogen removed by burning

6. A group of students designed the following apparatus to compare the viscosities of different liquids.

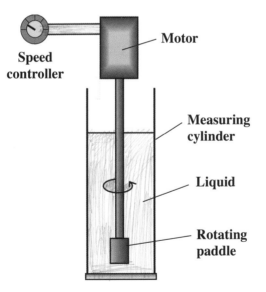

Motor

Speed controller

Measuring cylinder

Liquid

Rotating paddle

Suggest how the apparatus could be used.

Problem solving: miscellaneous

1. The first step in the industrial extraction of aluminium is to obtain aluminium oxide from the ore called bauxite.

   The ore is crushed. It is then digested, under pressure, with sodium hydroxide solution. The resulting mixture is filtered and the residue (containing large amounts of iron(III) oxide) is removed. The filtrate is seeded with a little aluminium oxide in order to produce large amounts of aluminium hydroxide. Sodium hydroxide solution is also formed. The aluminium hydroxide passes to a rotary kiln where it is roasted to form pure aluminium oxide.

   The flow chart summarises the production of aluminium oxide.

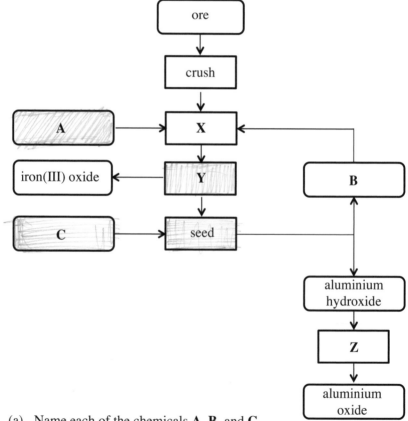

   (a) Name each of the chemicals **A**, **B**, and **C**.
   (b) Give a name for each of the processes **X**, **Y**, and **Z**.

2. Sulphuric acid can be prepared in industry by the Chamber Process. The following chemical reactions are involved.

* Sulphur is burned to produce sulphur dioxide.
* Sulphur dioxide reacts with water to produce sulphurous acid.
* Nitric oxide is produced by the catalytic oxidation of ammonia; water is also a product of this reaction.
* Nitric oxide reacts with oxygen to form nitrogen dioxide.
* Nitrogen dioxide reacts with sulphurous acid to form sulphuric acid and regenerate nitric oxide.

The flow diagram shows the production of sulphuric acid by the Chamber Process.

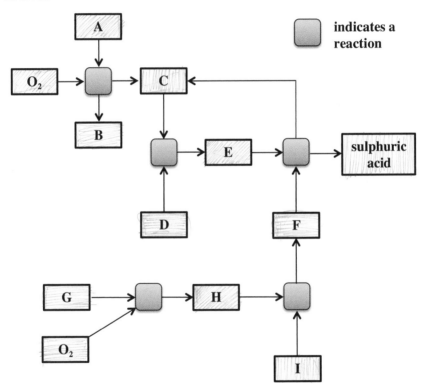

Name each of the chemicals **A** to **I**.

3. Acetone, widely used as a solvent, is manufactured from **cumene**. The feedstock is oxidised by air to form **cumene hydroperoxide**. The decomposition of this compound produces a mixture of **acetone** and **phenol** which is separated by distillation.

Draw a flow chart to summarise the manufacture of acetone from cumene.

In your flow chart use to represent chemicals

and [ ] to represent processes.

4. Prefixes can be used to indicate the number of atoms in a molecule.

Term	Number of atoms per molecule	Example
diatomic	2	hydrogen chloride
triatomic	3	carbon dioxide
tetra-atomic	4	sulphur trioxide
penta-atomic	5	tetrachloromethane
hexa-atomic	6	phosphorus pentachloride

(a) What term is used to describe the molecule shown?

```
    H
    |
    B
  /   \
H      H
```

(b) Name a hexa-atomic molecule, containing carbon, that will decolourise bromine water.

(c) Write a formula for a carbon compound consisting of penta-atomic molecules with a molecular mass of 85.

5. The structural formulae for some acids containing oxygen are shown.

Acid	Strength	Structure
nitric	strong	$O=N-OH$ with second O
nitrous	weak	$O=N-OH$
sulphuric	strong	structure of S with two O and two OH
sulphurous	weak	$O=S$ with two OH

(a) What structural feature appears to determine the strength of these acids?

(b) Chloric acid, $HClO_3$, is a strong acid.
Draw its full structural formula.

6. The idea of oxidation number leads to a systematic method of naming inorganic compounds. The systematic name of $KClO_3$ is potassium chlorate(V) where the Roman numeral in brackets represents the oxidation number of the chlorine atom.

Simplified rules for working out the oxidation numbers are:

all Group 1 metals have an oxidation number of +1;

oxygen has an oxidation number of -2;

the sum of the oxidation numbers of all atoms in the formula of a compound is zero.

Give the information corresponding to each of **A, B, C, D** and **E** that would complete the table below.

Formula	Oxidation number of non-oxygen atom in the negative ion	Systematic name	Negative ion charge
$KClO_3$	+5	Potassium chlorate(V)	1-
Na_2SO_4	+6	**A**	2-
B	+7	Potassium iodate(VII)	1-
Na_3PO_4	**C**	**D**	**E**

7. Complex ions are formed when molecules or ions join to a central metal ion by means of co-ordinate bonds.

The molecules or ions joining the central metal ion are called ligands and the total number of bonds being made to the central ion is known as the co-ordination number.

The charge of the complex ion is the combined charges of the central ion and the ligands.

(a) Give the information corresponding to each of **P, Q, R** and **S** that would complete the table below.

Central metal ion	Ligand	Co-ordination number	Structure of complex ion	Charge of complex ion
Al^{3+}	F^-	**P**	$$\begin{array}{c} F \\ | \quad F \\ F-Al-F \\ F \quad | \\ \quad F \end{array}$$	3-
Q	NH_3	4	$$\begin{array}{c} NH_3 \\ | \\ H_3N-Cu-NH_3 \\ | \\ NH_3 \end{array}$$	2+
Fe^{2+}	CN^-	6	$$\begin{array}{c} CN \\ | \quad CN \\ NC-Fe-CN \\ NC \quad | \\ \quad CN \end{array}$$	**R**
Co^{2+}	**S**	6	$$\begin{array}{c} CH_2-CH_2 \\ | \quad | \\ NH_2 \quad NH_2 \\ NH_2 \quad Co-NH_2 \\ CH_2 \quad NH_2 \quad NH_2 \quad CH_2 \\ CH_2 \quad \quad CH_2 \end{array}$$	2+

(b) A coloured complex ion is formed when solutions of nickel(II) sulphate react with solutions of ammonia.
The colour is most intense when the concentration of complex ions is greatest.
The graph shows the colour intensity when different volumes of equimolar nickel(II) sulphate and ammonia react.

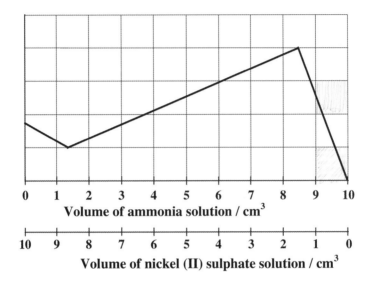

i) Describe how a student could have carried out this experiment.
ii) What ratio of ammonia to nickel(II) sulphate gives the highest colour intensity?

8.

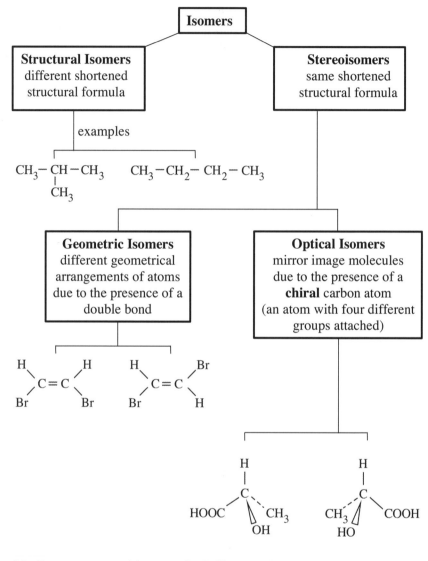

(a) Draw a structural isomer of 1,2-dibromoethane.
(b) Draw the geometric isomers of but-2-ene.
(c) Copy and complete the diagram to show the
    lightest alkane molecule containing a **chiral** carbon atom.

9. In a mass spectrometer, the energy of an electron beam can break bonds in molecules to form fragments containing groups of atoms. The positions of the peaks (or lines) in a mass spectrum correspond to the masses of the fragments that are formed.

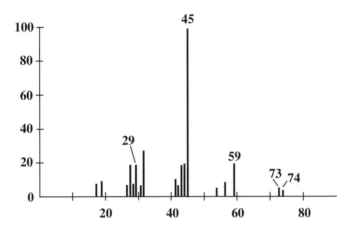

In the mass spectrum shown, the peaks at masses 29, 45, and 59 are formed by the breaking of carbon to carbon bonds in:

$$H-\underset{\underset{H}{|}}{\overset{\overset{H}{|}}{C}}-\underset{\underset{H}{|}}{\overset{\overset{H}{|}}{C}}-\underset{\underset{OH}{|}}{\overset{\overset{H}{|}}{C}}-\underset{\underset{H}{|}}{\overset{\overset{H}{|}}{C}}-H$$

a) Give the information corresponding to each of **F** and **G** in the table below.

Relative mass	Formula of fragment
29	C_2H_5
45	**F**
59	**G**

b) Suggest what causes the peaks at masses just below the main peak at 45, e.g. at 44, 43, 42 and 41.

10. X-ray diffraction is a technique used to determine the structure of molecules. It is the electrons in the atoms of the molecule which diffract the X-rays. From the diffraction pattern, an electron-density contour map of the molecule can be constructed.
The following map was obtained using a carbon compound with molecular formula $C_6H_9Cl_3O$.

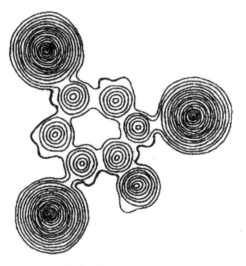

(a) Suggest why the hydrogen atoms do not show up clearly in the electron-density contour map.

(b) Draw the full structural formula for this compound.

(c) Draw the electron-density contour map that would be obtained for methanoic acid:

11. The bonds in organic molecules absorb infra-red radiation. The same bond in different molecules always absorbs infra-red radiation of similar wavenumber. For example, the C-H bond absorbs in the range 2800-3000 wavenumbers (cm⁻¹).

    The following diagrams (from SDBS Information) refer to three different organic liquids.

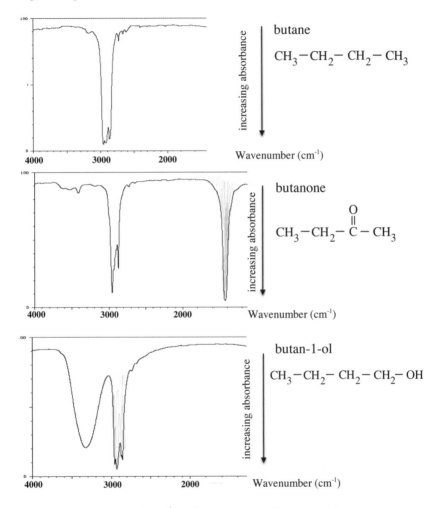

(a) The absorption at 1710 cm⁻¹ in the spectrum of butanone is absent from the spectrum of butane and butan-1-ol.
    Which bond could be responsible for this absorption?

(b) Sketch a graph to show the absorptions you would predict for butanoic acid.

12. Differential thermal analysis (DTA) is a technique used to investigate changes that occur in substances when they are heated. This technique involves measuring the temperature difference between a test substance and a reference substance when both are heated.

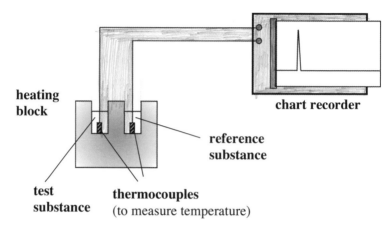

As soon as a change occurs in the test substance, its temperature (T_T) will differ from that of the reference substance (T_R). The following DTA curve was obtained when using calcium oxalate (CaC_2O_4) as the test substance.

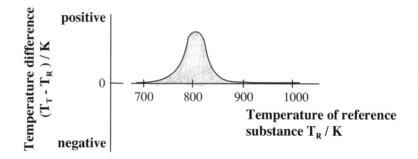

The peak corresponds to the change: $CaC_2O_4 \rightarrow CaCO_3 + CO$
This change occurs at 725 K.
(a) Why can it be concluded that the rise in the DTA curve is due to the change being exothermic?
(b) Suggest a property that a substance must have to make it suitable as a reference substance in DTA analysis.
(c) Selenium melts at 490 K.
Draw the DTA curve that would be expected if selenium was heated in the DTA apparatus in the range 440 K to 700 K.

Chemistry in Society

13. An acid can be thought of as a chemical which can release H^+ (aq) ions.
    In an acid-base reaction the H^+ (aq) ions released by the acid are accepted
    by the base.
    Some acid-base reactions are reversible. In these reactions both forward
    and reverse reactions involve the transfer of H^+ (aq) ions from the acid to
    the base.
    (a) Using the information given above, complete the table showing the
        acid and base provided when OH^- ions react with H_3O^+ ion.

Acid	Base		Acid	Base
H_2O	NH_3	$\rightleftharpoons$	NH_4^+	HS^-
H_3O^+	OH^-	$\rightleftharpoons$		

(b) Another reversible acid-base reaction is shown.

$$HCO^{3-} \quad + \quad OH^- \quad \rightleftharpoons \quad CO_3^{2-} \quad + \quad H_2O$$

In the reverse reaction, state whether the water is acting as an acid or
as a base.

14. Nuclear magnetic resonance spectroscopy (NMR) is a widely used analytical chemical technique. Detailed information can be obtained about the numbers of hydrogen atoms and their environment within a molecule. The molecules under investigation are placed in a powerful magnetic field and a band of radio frequencies is applied. The emitted radiation is analysed for absorptions by the hydrogen atoms.

The height of the absorption peak produced is directly proportional to the number of hydrogen atoms in a particular environment.

Each different environment produces absorptions at a slightly different frequency. The position of each absorption is given as a 'chemical shift' from the position at which the hydrogen atoms in a reference standard adsorbs.

Hydrogen atom environment	Chemical shift relative to reference standard
$-CH_3$ (in an alkane)	0.9
$-CH_2-$ (in an alkane)	1.3
$-CH-$ (in an alkane)	2.0
CH_3-O- (in an alcohol)	3.8
$-O-H$ (in an alcohol)	5.0

An NMR spectrum of methyl propane is as follows.

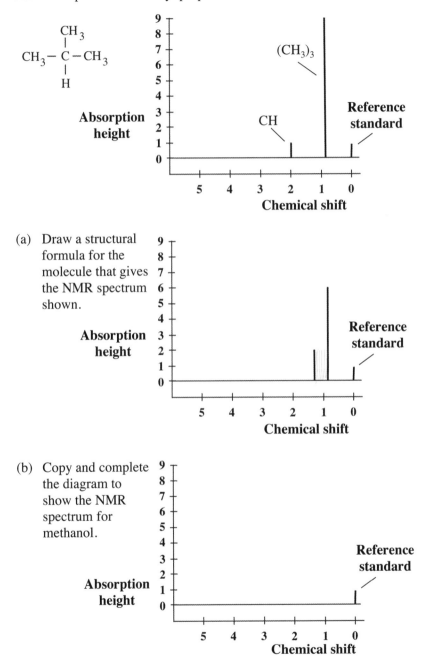

(a) Draw a structural formula for the molecule that gives the NMR spectrum shown.

(b) Copy and complete the diagram to show the NMR spectrum for methanol.

15. The structure of an ionic compound consists of a giant lattice of oppositely charged ions. The arrangement of ions is mainly determined by the "radius ratio' of the ions involved.

$$\text{Radius ratio} = \frac{\text{radius of positive ion}}{\text{radius of negative ion}}$$

The arrangements for caesium chloride, CsCl, and sodium chloride, NaCl, are shown below.

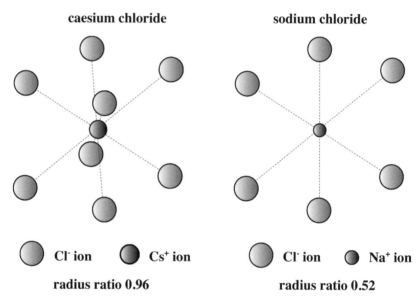

caesium chloride

sodium chloride

Cl⁻ ion   Cs⁺ ion   Cl⁻ ion   Na⁺ ion

radius ratio 0.96   **radius ratio 0.52**

(a) By using the table of ionic radii in the Data Booklet, calculate the radius ratio for magnesium oxide, MgO, and state which of the two arrangements, caesium chloride or sodium chloride, it is more likely to adopt.

(b) The enthalpy of lattice breaking is the energy required to completely separate the ions from one mole of an ionic solid.

Ions	F⁻	Cl⁻	Br⁻
Li⁺	1030	834	788
Na⁺	910	769	732
K⁺	808	701	671

Write a general statement linking the enthalpy of lattice breaking to ion size.

Chemical arithmetic

1. Iron can be extracted from cornflakes.
   (a) The mass of iron in four 40 cm³ servings of cornflakes is shown in the table.

Sample	Mass of iron/mg
1	3.2
2	3.0
3	2.6
4	3.4

   Calculate the average mass of iron in the four servings.

   (b) A recommended daily allowance (RDA) of iron is 8.0 mg.

   Calculate the percentage of the RDA that can be obtained from serving 1.

2. A recommended daily allowance (RDA) for vitamin C is 80 mg. A packet of cereal shows that a 100 g portion contained 48 mg of vitamin C. Calculate the mass of the cereal required to give 30% of the RDA for vitamin C.

3. A sample of air contains 78.7% of nitrogen.

   Calculate the mass of liquid air needed to obtain 300 000 kg of nitrogen.

4. A recommended daily allowance (RDA) for calcium is 1000 mg. A carton of milk contains 124 mg of calcium per 100 cm³.

   Calculate the percentage of the RDA that is provided by 250 cm³ of milk from the carton.

5. A bottle for treating indigestion contained 7.4 g of the active ingredient in 200 cm³ of a liquid mixture. The maximum dose of the active ingredient in a 24 hour period is 500 mg.

   Calculate the maximum volume of the liquid mixture that could be taken over 12 hours.

6. The alcohol limit for driving in Scotland is 50 mg per 100 cm^3 of blood. At 10.00 pm, a man stopped drinking and had 56 mg of alcohol per 100 cm^3 of blood. Alcohol was removed from his body at a constant rate of 16 mg per 100 cm^3 of blood per hour.

   Calculate the time for his alcohol level to reach 40% of the alcohol limit for driving.

7. Methanol is a fuel (that was once) used as an alternative to petrol in racing cars. A car had a 45 litre tank that costs £90 to fill.

   Use the information below to calculate the cost of methanol required to produce 2.4 x 10^5 kJ.

Mass of 1 cm^3 of methanol	0.792 g
Energy from 1 g of methanol	21.3 kJ

8. Oxygen makes up 20.95% of dry air by volume. Oxygen can be removed from the air by cooling the air until it is liquid and then distilling the liquid air.

   Use the density of oxygen given in the Data Booklet to calculate the volume of liquid air required to produce 100 kg of oxygen.

9. A model steam-train uses ethanol as a fuel. The energy produced for moving the train by the burning of ethanol is 24.6 kJ per gram of ethanol. A bottle of ethanol, volume 2 litres, costs £9.36. The density of ethanol is 0.79 g/cm^3.

   Calculate the cost of ethanol that would burn to produce 15 000 kJ of energy.

10. Cashew nuts are a source of zinc and provide 1.4 mg per 25 g of cashew nuts. A recommended daily allowance (RDA) for zinc is 10.0 mg. A 175 g packet of cashew nuts cost £1.37.

    Calculate the cost of cashew nuts that will provide 50% of the RDA for zinc.

11. A packet of medicinal sweets contains 36 lozenges. Each lozenge contains 5.4 mg of the active ingredients. The mass of the lozenges in the packet is 134 g.

Calculate the percentage by mass of the active ingredients in 1 lozenge.

12. There are four steps that can be followed in order to calculate the melt value of a gold piece:
    1. *First, determine the mass of the piece in grams.*
    2. *Second, establish the quality of the gold piece. Gold purity is traditionally indicated in karats, which measures the gold purity on a scale of 1 to 24, e.g. a 12 karat piece would be 50% pure, giving a quality of 0.5.*
    3. *Thirdly, find the current gold price (usually quoted per troy ounce) and calculate the price per gram. One troy ounce is equal to 31.1 grams.*
    4. *Finally, calculate the melt value of the piece by multiplying together the values for the mass, the quality and the price per gram.*

Calculate the melt value of a 4 carat gold piece with a mass of 450 g, assuming a gold price of £840 per troy ounce.

13. A forensic scientist proved that Dr Crippen used a poison called hyoscine to murder his wife. From the remains, the scientist extracted 2 mg of the poison from the stomach, 1.6 mg from the kidneys, 5.4 mg from the liver and 9 mg from the intestines.
    It was believed that the mass of hyoscine extracted was 58% of the fatal dose.
    Crippen bought 5 grains of hyoscine that, at today's prices, would cost £13.50. The mass of hyoscine in a grain was 64 mg.
    (a) Calculate the average mass extracted over the four sites.
    (b) Calculate the mass of hyoscine in the fatal dose.
    (c) Calculate the total cost, at today's prices, of the hyoscine extracted from the remains.

Open questions

1. The element hydrogen is found in molecules that can have both pure covalent and polar covalent bonding. Hydrogen is also found in ionic compounds known as hydrides.

   Using your knowledge of chemistry, comment on molecules and ionic compounds containing hydrogen.

2. Ammonia is manufactured in industry by the Haber Process.

   Using your knowledge of chemistry, comment on the way that the process is designed to maximise both yield and profit and minimise the damaging impact on the environment.

3. A technician made up a list of liquids for use as solvents. The following liquids were on the list:

   ethanol, ethyl ethanoate, hexane, propanone, water

   Using your knowledge of chemistry, comment on the use of the liquids for making solutions in the lab.

4. Gravy granules can contain a mixture of covalent and ionic compounds.

   Using your knowledge of chemistry, describe ways to show that both covalent and ionic compounds are present in gravy granules.

5. Chemical reactions involving water are all around us … in everyday life, in industry as well as in the laboratory. With some of these reactions, the name given to the type of reaction gives a clue to the involvement of water.

   Using your knowledge of chemistry, comment on the use of water as a reactant or product in chemical reactions.

6. Cast iron wood burning stoves and traditional coal burning fireplaces are both used to burn fuels in domestic properties. The wood burning stoves have a greater airflow and in some cases make use of a catalyst.

   Using your knowledge of chemistry, suggest why wood burning stoves are considered to be more efficient and environmentally friendly.